Radioisotope Experiments for Schools and Colleges

D1247568

Radioisotope Experiments for Schools and Colleges

J. B. DANCE, M.Sc.

Lecturer in Physical Science, Bromsgrove College of Further Education. Formerly of A.E.R.E., Harwell

OXFORD · LONDON · EDINBURGH · NEW YORK
TORONTO · SYDNEY · PARIS · BRAUNSCHWEIG

Pergamon Press Ltd., Headington Hill Hall, Oxford
4 & 5 Fitzroy Square, London W.1

Pergamon Press (Scotland) Ltd., 2 & 3 Teviot Place, Edinburgh 1

Pergamon Press Inc., 44–01 21st Street, Long Island City, New York 11101

Pergamon of Canada, Ltd., 6 Adelaide Street East, Toronto, Ontario

Pergamon Press (Aust.) Pty. Ltd., 20–22 Margaret Street,
Sydney, New South Wales

Pergamon Press S.A.R.L., 24 rue des Écoles, Paris 5e

Vieweg & Sohn GmbH, Burgplatz 1, Braunschweig

Printed in Great Britain by A. Wheaton & Co. Ltd., Exeter and London

Contents

1. FUNDAMENTALS   1

The discovery of radioactivity. Atomic structure. Types of radioactive change. Decay kinetics. The Curie. The interaction of radiation with matter. Bremsstrahlung. Gamma radiation. Isotope production.

2. THE MEASUREMENT OF NUCLEAR RADIATION   16

Geiger counters. Scintillation detectors. Semiconductor detectors. Scalers. Statistics of counting. Resolving time. Background counts. Ratemeters. Absolute and relative counting. Absorption measurements. Self-absorption. The pocket dosimeter. The quartz fibre ionisation chamber. The pulse electroscope.

3. NATURALLY OCCURRING RADIOISOTOPES   43

Natural radioactive series. Radioactive equilibrium. Branching chains. Uranium compounds. Thorium. The emanations. Other natural radioisotopes.

4. HEALTH PHYSICS   55

Radiation and contamination. Dose units. Maximum permissible doses. Dose rate calculations. Beta and gamma dose rates. Precautions in the use of closed sources. Measurement of gamma dose rate. Contamination. Precautions in the use of unsealed isotopes. Monitoring. Maximum permissible levels. Film badge service.

8. EXPERIMENTS USING SEALED SOURCES   153

9. EXPERIMENTS USING UNSEALED ARTIFICIALLY PRODUCED ISOTOPES   159

Preface

DURING the past few years there has been a definite trend in all types of British educational establishments towards the teaching of "modern" physics, including simple experimental work with radioisotopes. At the time of writing the Association for Science Education is preparing a report on the teaching of radiochemistry and it seems probable that considerably more work with radio-isotopes will be carried out in chemistry (and, to some extent, in biology) at sixth-form level and above.

One of the most important reasons for including radioisotope work in a syllabus is that it provides one of the very few ways in which individual atomic events manifest themselves and there-fore provides very convincing evidence of the particulate nature of matter. It is a subject which can include such diverse fields as statistics, electronics, photography, health physics, botany, etc. Suitable experimental work can be arranged for students at almost any level from G.C.E. O-level upwards.

Experimental work with small sealed sources suitable for use with Geiger tubes presents a very small health hazard since there is no contamination danger and the dose rates at a foot or more from such a source are very small. The annual integrated dose will also be very small, since it is not likely that a person will spend more than about 20 hours per week within 2 feet of such a source.

The main hazard arises from the use of unsealed sources which can result in the contamination of other objects and of people. Ideally all unsealed radioisotope work should be carried out in a laboratory reserved for this purpose, but few schools and few of the smaller colleges can allocate even a small laboratory exclusively for this purpose. It is the main aim of this book to show that a reasonably complete elementary course can be given using only naturally occurring radioisotopes and a few sealed sources of artificially produced nuclides. The naturally occurring radioisotopes (which are readily available from normal chemical suppliers) have a very small specific activity and present an almost negligible contamination hazard. Indeed, their chemical toxicity is greater than their radiotoxicity. Even in the larger colleges and universities the use of naturally occurring isotopes provides a very useful and safe introduction to the use of unsealed sources. Nevertheless, a few typical experiments in which unsealed artificially produced nuclides are used will be described for completeness. Establishments which do not have good facilities available may minimise contamination hazards by purchasing unsealed isotopes in tablet form.

The equipment required for most of the experiments discussed in this book is simple Geiger counting equipment or photographic emulsions, but a few experiments using other forms of detectors which are often found in schools (such as pulse electroscopes) are included. No scintillation, proportional or semiconductor detectors are necessary for any of the experiments, although the sensitivity may in some cases be increased by the use of a scintillation detector for gamma radiation.

Students in G.C.E. A-level courses will obviously not have enough time to carry out all of the experiments described. It is suggested that some of the most suitable experiments for an A-level course in physics are some of those of Chapter 6 together with the short Experiments 7.1, 7.5 and 7.8 or 7.13 and possibly Experiments 8.1, 8.2 and 8.3. Experiment 7.2 is especially suitable for students interested in electronics; Experiment 7.3 for those interested in mathematics, whilst Experiments 7.8 to 7.11, 7.15 to 7.17 and 7.19 to 7.23 are very suitable for those intending to specialise in chemistry. Unsealed artificially produced nuclides are required for almost all biological experiments (see Experiments 9.5 and 9.6).

The basic ideas for most of the experiments to be described are not, of course, original, but the experiments have been modified in various ways to render them more suitable for elementary courses where only simple equipment is available. Some of the experiments (such as the separation of UX_1 or ThX by precipitation and the collection of ^{212}Pb by electrodeposition) have developed from the work of various laboratories early in this century. Other experiments have been developed at various teaching establishments and many variations of them have been published without acknowledgement. For this reason it has not proved possible to trace the originators of the basic ideas for many of the experiments in order to make appropriate acknowledgements. However, the writer would be pleased to hear from anyone who feels that the idea for any experiment he has originated has been included in this book so that appropriate acknowledgement may be made in any future edition.

Alcester,   J. B. DANCE
Warwickshire.
June 1966

Acknowledgements

THE author is indebted to B. Taylor, Esq., and to the following companies for providing photographs which have been included in this book: Griffin & George Ltd.; Isotope Developments Ltd.; Jonpar Electronics; Nucleonic Accessories Ltd.; Panax Equipment Ltd.; Research Electronics Ltd.; and Twentieth Century Electronics Ltd.

Acknowledgement is made to Panax Equipment Ltd. for permission to reproduce Experiment 7.13 and to Oxford University Press for permission to reproduce Experiments 7.17 and 7.23 which are modified versions of experiments originally published in *Modern Radiochemical Practice* by G. B. Cook and J. F. Duncan. The author is also grateful to K. J. Norman, Esq., of the United Kingdom Atomic Energy Authority (Risley) for data on the isotopic composition of the "depleted" uranium supplied by the Authority to chemical manufacturers.

The author is also indebted to the following persons who have kindly sent him manuals of experiments developed at their establishments or details of various experiments: Mr. R. A. Faires, the Isotope School, the United Kingdom Atomic Energy Authority, Wantage, Berkshire, England. Dr. R. T. Overman, the Oak Ridge Institute of Nuclear Studies, the United States Atomic Energy Commission, Oak Ridge, Tennessee, U.S.A. Prof. Dr. W. Seelmann-Eggebert, Kernforschungszentrum, Karlsruhe, Germany. Dr. H. Münzel, Kernreaktor Bau- und Betriebs-Gesellschaft M.B.H., Karlsruhe, Germany.

CHAPTER 1

Fundamentals

The Discovery of Radioactivity

Uranium was discovered as long ago as 1782 by Klaproth, but the phenomenon of radioactivity was not found until 1896 when Henri Becquerel was studying the properties of potassium uranyl sulphate, K_2SO_4, UO_2SO_4, $2H_2O$. X-rays (which had been discovered during the previous year) were known to cause this double sulphate to give out light or fluoresce. Becquerel arranged an experiment of the reverse type to try to ascertain whether X-rays or any other form of penetrating radiation was given out when sunlight fell onto crystals of the double sulphate.

He wrapped a photographic plate in black paper and placed some crystals of potassium uranyl sulphate on the paper. The crystals were then exposed to sunlight for some time. On development the plate showed dark areas at points near to which the crystals had been placed. Becquerel found that the radiation from the material would pass through thin layers of many substances, but he was puzzled when he discovered that a photographic plate was darkened even if the crystals were made in the dark and were never exposed to light. The continuous production of energy by the uranium salt seemed inexplicable. It was soon discovered that the effect on a photographic plate was proportional to the amount of the uranium in the material, but did not depend on its chemical form.

X-rays ionise air and allow the charge on an electroscope to leak away. It was found that the radiation emitted by uranium-containing compounds also discharged electroscopes and this provided another means of detecting it. In 1898 thorium

1

compounds were found to give out a similar type of radiation. A year later Rutherford showed that more than one type of radiation was emitted from radioactive materials. The type which produced the most intense ionisation was completely absorbed by a thin aluminium foil and was called alpha radiation. Beta radiation is more penetrating and will pass through a fairly thin sheet of aluminium. These types of radiation are deflected in opposite directions by a magnetic field. The direction of deflection showed that alpha rays are positively charged and beta rays negatively charged. A third type of radiation known as gamma radiation was discovered by Villard in 1900. It is considerably more penetrating than either alpha or beta radiation, but causes less ionisation and is not deflected by a magnetic field.

Other radioactive elements were separated chemically from uranium ores, the best-known example being the separation of radium by the Curies. The practical separation of various radioactive materials from uranium and thorium compounds will be discussed in later chapters.

Atomic Structure

In order to understand the behaviour of radioactive atoms it is necessary to have a basic knowledge of the structure of atoms and nuclei. An atom may be considered to be one or more electrons travelling around a central nucleus. Only the outer electrons take part in chemical changes, the inner electrons and the nucleus remaining quite unaffected. The nucleus has been shown to consist of a number of protons and neutrons held together by very powerful (but short range) nuclear forces. In a neutral atom the number of negative electrons is equal to the number of positive protons. This number determines the chemical properties of the atom. Under normal conditions an atom cannot gain or lose a proton from its nucleus, but it will gain or lose electrons fairly easily. Atoms are therefore characterised by the number of protons present in their nuclei, this number being known as the atomic number.

Let us consider the simplest atom with an atomic number of one, namely hydrogen. Ordinary hydrogen (Fig. 1.1a) consists of a single proton and a single electron. However, another form of hydrogen exists which is known as deuterium (Fig. 1.1b). This

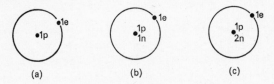

FIG. 1.1. The three isotopes of hydrogen.

has one proton and one neutron in its nucleus. The neutral atom must also have one electron or it would not have the same chemical properties as ordinary hydrogen. A third type of hydrogen, known as tritium, has also been found (Fig. 1.1c). This form of hydrogen, which is radioactive, contains two neutrons and one proton in its nucleus.

The three forms of hydrogen have exactly similar chemical properties, the main difference between them being their weight. The weight of a neutron is little greater than that of a proton, but is very much greater than that of an electron (actually about 1836 times greater). Thus the weights of the three atoms are in the approximate ratio 1:2:3. They are often called hydrogen-1, hydrogen-2 and hydrogen-3 to show their approximate atomic weights. In symbol form they are written ^1H, ^2H and ^3H. If it is also desired to show the atomic number, they may be written ^1_1H, ^2_1H and ^3_1H; however, the symbol H itself implies that the atomic number is one. The forms of an element with different atomic weights (but the same atomic number) are known as isotopes of the element. A species in which the atomic weight and atomic number are both specified is known as a nuclide.

The atomic weight of any isotope approximates to a whole number. This whole number is known as the mass number of the nuclide and is shown in such symbols as ^3H, ^{14}C, ^{238}U, etc.

As a further example the isotopes of carbon may be considered. The atomic number of carbon is 6 and the atomic weights range from 10 to 15. The isotopes are $^{10}_{6}C$ (6 protons and 4 neutrons in the nucleus), $^{11}_{6}C$ (6p, 5n), $^{12}_{6}C$ (6p, 6n), $^{13}_{6}C$ (6p, 7n), $^{14}_{6}C$ (6p, 8n) and $^{15}_{6}C$ (6p, 9n). The only ones which are not radioactive are ^{12}C and ^{13}C.

If there is more than one naturally occurring isotope of an element, in most cases all natural specimens of that element contain the same proportion of each isotope. For example, chlorine obtained from natural sources consists of a mixture of ^{35}Cl with about one-quarter of its weight of ^{37}Cl; the mean atomic weight of any specimen of natural chlorine is 35·46. Exceptions occur when one particular isotope is being formed by the decay of a natural radioactive element or by the bombardment of atoms by cosmic rays from space. In this case the atomic weight of various specimens of an element may vary.

Types of Radioactive Change

If the nucleus of an atom has too much energy to be stable, it will lose some energy by the emission of radiation. The various types of radioactive change which can occur are discussed below. Some types of atom decay solely by one mechanism, whereas in other cases a fraction of the atoms will decay in one way and a fraction in another way.

1. *Alpha Decay*

Alpha radiation has been shown to consist of fast-moving helium nuclei (two protons combined with two neutrons). Many of the very heavy nuclei emit alpha particles. For example, the most common isotope of uranium, ^{238}U, is an alpha emitter which decays according to the equation

$$^{238}_{92}U \longrightarrow {}^{234}_{90}Th + {}^{4}_{2}He$$
$$\text{(alpha particle)}$$

Both the atomic weights and the atomic numbers must balance on each side of the equation. Therefore if a nucleus emits an alpha particle it loses four atomic weight units and its atomic number falls by two; another element is therefore formed. The product atom in the above equation is itself radioactive; it is an isotope of ordinary thorium (^{232}Th).

2. Beta Decay

Ordinary beta radiation consists of high energy electrons moving with a velocity approaching that of light. In a neutron-rich nucleus the following transformation can occur resulting in the formation of a beta particle:

$$^1_0n \longrightarrow\ ^1_1p\ +\ ^{\ 0}_{-1}e\ +\ ^{0-}_0\nu$$

neutron   proton   beta   antineutrino
                     particle

The energy of the reaction is divided between the beta particle and the antineutrino, but it is almost impossible to detect the latter. Carbon-14 undergoes beta decay, the reaction being written as follows:

$$^{14}_6C \longrightarrow\ ^{14}_7N\ +\ ^{\ 0}_{-1}e\ +\ ^{0-}_0\nu$$

It should be noted that the atom produced in this reaction has one more proton and one less neutron than the original atom. Thus in beta decay the atomic weight remains constant whilst the atomic number increases by unity.

3. Positron Decay (or Positive Beta Decay)

If a nucleus has too many protons for stability, it may decay with the emission of a positive electron or positron. The basic reaction is

$$^1_1p \longrightarrow\ ^1_0n\ +\ ^{\ 0}_{+1}e\ +\ ^0_0\nu$$

proton   neutron   positron   neutrino

It is virtually impossible to detect the neutrino, but the positron can be detected with a Geiger counter. In the case of the proton rich ^{11}C, the equation may be written

$$^{11}_{6}C \longrightarrow {}^{11}_{5}B + {}^{0}_{+1}e + {}^{0}_{0}\nu$$

4. *Electron Capture*

An alternative way in which a proton-rich nucleus can become stable involves the capture of an orbital electron, normally from the innermost (K) orbital. It is often called K capture.

$$^{1}_{1}p + {}^{0}_{-1}e \longrightarrow {}^{1}_{0}n + {}^{0}_{0}\nu$$

In both positron decay and electron capture, the atom produced has the same atomic weight as the original atom, but the atomic number is reduced by unity.

5. *Gamma Emission*

Gamma rays, like light, are electromagnetic radiation but are of very high frequency (very short wavelength). In any type of radioactive change a nucleus may be left which has too much energy to be stable. This excess energy is often emitted as a gamma ray or gamma photon within a very short time. For example, cobalt-60 is a beta emitter which decays as follows:

$$^{60}_{27}Co \longrightarrow {}^{60}_{28}Ni + {}^{0}_{-1}e + {}^{0}_{0}\bar{\nu}$$

The nickel-60 atom thus formed is left in an excited state and within a very minute fraction of a second it emits two gamma rays in succession. The cobalt-60 is normally referred to as an emitter of beta and gamma rays, although it is actually the excited product nucleus which emits the gamma radiation.

In some cases the emission of a gamma ray does not occur until some time after the emission of a beta ray. For example, caesium-137 decays into an excited form of barium-137 which usually emits a gamma ray within a few minutes. The excited state is known as metastable barium-137 or ^{137m}Ba and is considered as a separate radioactive nuclide.

When gamma emission occurs, the product nucleus has the same atomic weight and the same atomic number as the original nucleus, but has less energy.

6. *Internal Conversion*

Internal conversion occurs when the energy of a gamma ray emitted from a nucleus is used to expel one of the orbital electrons from the atom. Another electron from one of the outer shells then fills the vacancy and an X-ray is emitted.

7. *Spontaneous Fission*

It is possible for nuclei of some of the heavy atoms to split into two parts, i.e. to undergo fission. The atoms produced carry a high energy and behave as radiation of low penetrating power.

In elementary work the most important types of radiation are alpha, beta and gamma radiation.

Decay Kinetics

A very convenient measure of the activity of a nuclide is the half-life, i.e. the time for one-half of the nuclide to decay away. After two half-lives one-quarter of the initial amount of the isotope will remain, after three half-lives one-eighth, and so on. The half-lives of the known radioactive materials vary over a very wide range from much less than a microsecond through values of hours and days up to over a thousand million million years. The shorter the half-life of a nuclide, the greater the activity of a given number of atoms. The rate of decay is unaffected by the conditions or the chemical form of an element. (A slight exception occurs in the case of electron capture nuclides whose rate of decay can be slightly altered by changes of chemical form.)

There is a certain probability that any atom of a radioisotope will decay within a certain time. This probability is unaffected by the past history of the atom or by the passage of time. Thus the rate of decay of a sample of a specified radionuclide is proportional to the number of atoms of that material present. If the number of atoms present at any time in a sample is N, the rate of decay may be represented in normal calculus notation as $-dN/dt$. The minus sign indicates that the number of atoms decreases as decay occurs. The rate of decay is proportional to the number of atoms present at the time in question, that is

$$-\frac{dN}{dt} \quad \propto \quad N$$

or

$$-\frac{dN}{dt} \quad = \quad \lambda N,$$

where λ is a constant for the particular nuclide concerned known as the radioactive constant.

$$\frac{dN}{N} \quad = \quad -\lambda dt. \tag{1.1}$$

Integrating,

$$\log_e N \quad = \quad -\lambda t \quad + \quad C,$$

where C is the constant of integration.

If $N = N_0$ when $t = 0$, $\log_e N_0 = C$.

Hence

$$\log_e N - \log_e N_0 = -\lambda t,$$

$$\log_e \frac{N}{N_0} \quad = \quad -\lambda t, \tag{1.2}$$

or

$$N = N_0 e^{-\lambda t}. \tag{1.3}$$

The half-life will now be found in terms of λ. If we denote the half-life by $t_{\frac{1}{2}}$, we can put $t = t_{\frac{1}{2}}$ into eqn. (1.3) when $N/N_0 = \frac{1}{2}$.

$$\frac{1}{2} = e^{-\lambda t_{\frac{1}{2}}}$$
$$\log_e \frac{1}{2} = -\lambda t_{\frac{1}{2}}$$
$$\log_e 2 = \lambda t_{\frac{1}{2}}$$
$$t_{\frac{1}{2}} = \frac{\log_e 2}{\lambda} = \frac{0 \cdot 69315}{\lambda}. \tag{1.4}$$

The Curie

The amount of radioactivity in a sample is expressed in curies. Originally the curie was defined in terms of a quantity of radon and was later defined as the amount of a radioactive material which undergoes the same number of disintegrations per second as 1 g of pure radium. According to this definition the value of the curie varied with the accuracy with which the radioactive constant of radium was known. In 1950 an international committee recommended that the curie be defined as the amount of any isotope which undergoes $3 \cdot 700 \times 10^{10}$ disintegrations/sec. This is now the generally accepted definition. One curie is approximately equal to the activity of 1 g of pure radium.

It should be noted that the curie is defined in terms of the number of disintegrations per second rather than in terms of the number of particles emitted. Cobalt-60 emits two gamma rays per disintegration and 1 curie of this material will therefore emit $2 \times 3 \cdot 700 \times 10^{10}$ gamma photons/sec. Similarly, if an element decays in more than one way, the number of particles of any one type emitted from 1 curie of the material may be less than $3 \cdot 700 \times 10^{10}$ per sec.

Another unit of activity which has been proposed is the rutherford. A source has an activity of 1 rutherford when it undergoes 10^6 disintegrations/sec. In spite of the fact that a unit of this size is generally more convenient than the curie, the rutherford is hardly ever used.

The weight of a radioisotope used in experimental work is

usually very small. Let us, for example, calculate the weight of iodine-131 in 1 mcurie of this material given that its half-life is 8·06 days.

$$\lambda = \frac{0\cdot693}{t_{\frac{1}{2}}} \quad \text{[see eqn. (1.4)]},$$

$$\lambda = \frac{0\cdot693}{8\cdot06} \text{ day}^{-1} = 9\cdot95 \times 10^{-7} \text{ sec}^{-1},$$

$$-\frac{dN}{dt} = 3\cdot70 \times 10^7 \text{ disintegrations/sec for 1 mcurie},$$

$$N = \frac{-\dfrac{dN}{dt}}{\lambda} \quad \text{[see eqn. (1.1)]},$$

$$N = \frac{3\cdot70 \times 10^7}{9\cdot95 \times 10^{-7}} = 3\cdot72 \times 10^{13} \text{ atoms/mcurie}.$$

There are $6\cdot023 \times 10^{23}$ atoms in 131 g of ^{131}I (Avogadro's number). Therefore weight of 1 mcurie

$$= \frac{3\cdot72 \times 10^{13}}{6\cdot02 \times 10^{23}} \times 131 = 8\cdot09 \times 10^{-9} \text{ g}.$$

The weight of 1 mcurie of a material varies considerably with the half-life, some examples being shown in Table 1.1.

TABLE 1.1

Isotope	Half-life	Weight of 1 mcurie (g)
^{204}Pb	$1\cdot4 \times 10^{17}$ years	$8\cdot0 \times 10^{10}$
^{238}U	$4\cdot51 \times 10^9$ years	2990
^{14}C	5570 years	$0\cdot22 \times 10^{-3}$
^{131}I	8·06 days	$8\cdot08 \times 10^{-9}$
^{212}Po	3×10^{-7} sec	$5\cdot6 \times 10^{-21}$

The Interaction of Radiation with Matter

Charged particles, including alpha and beta particles, are slowed down as they pass through matter, their energy being used to create ions and excited atoms in the material through which they are passing. If the material is thick enough, the particles will be completely absorbed in it and will become part of the substance. The higher the initial energy of a particle, the farther it will pass through a given material. Particle energies are conveniently measured in millions of electron volts (MeV) or thousands of electron volts (keV). One electron volt is the energy change occurring when an electron moves through a potential difference of one volt.

Alpha particles rapidly lose their energy in any material, even in a gas at atmospheric pressure, and a large number of ions per centimetre are therefore formed along an alpha particle track. A 3 MeV alpha particle will travel a distance of about $1 \cdot 67$ cm in air, whereas a 5 MeV alpha particle will travel about $3 \cdot 51$ cm in air at normal pressure.

The thickness of an absorbing material is conveniently expressed in grammes per square centimetre (g/cm^2) or in milligrammes per square centimetre (mg/cm^2). The number of mg/cm^2 of a material through which a charged particle will pass is essentially independent of the nature of the material, although it is very dependent on the type of particle and on the particle energy. The range of an alpha particle in air, R cm, is given by the following approximate expression:

$$R = 0 \cdot 322E^{3/2},$$

where E is the energy of the particle in megaelectron volts. The energy of the alpha particles emitted by a radioisotope has a limited number of definite values which are determined by the differences in the energy levels of the nuclei concerned.

A beta particle does not lose nearly so much energy per centimetre of its path as an alpha particle and it can therefore travel much further before it is completely absorbed. A typical beta particle will travel some metres in air. The beta particles from a single radioisotope have a wide range of energies, since the available energy is shared between the beta particle and the neutrino which is emitted with it. Thus a beta particle may have an energy of any value up to a certain maximum which is characteristic of the nuclide concerned. Tritium emits only low energy beta particles with a maximum energy of about 18 keV, whereas the maximum energy of the beta particles emitted by potassium-42 is 3·6 MeV. Thus the particles from tritium will penetrate only extremely thin layers of material, whereas a considerable proportion of those from potassium-42 will penetrate a thickness of 0·5 cm of aluminium. If the thickness of material through which some beta particles will just pass is measured, the results may be used to estimate the energy of the beta radiation, and this assists in the identification of the emitting radioisotope.

Bremsstrahlung

When beta radiation passes through matter, some of the energy of the radiation is converted into a type of electromagnetic radiation known as "bremsstrahlung". This type of radiation is caused by the deceleration of beta particles in the electric field surrounding the nuclei of the matter through which they are passing. The name Bremsstrahlung is the German for "braking radiation" (from the verb *bremsen*, to brake).

Bremsstrahlung is similar to gamma radiation except that it has a continuous energy spectrum and (when produced by beta particles of normal energy) is not very penetrating, since the mean energy is fairly low. The amount of bremsstrahlung produced when beta particles strike a material containing nuclei of high atomic number is very much greater than when the material contains only atoms of low atomic number. The efficiency of the conversion of beta particle energy is, however, normally quite low, and bremsstrahlung is usually important only in the case of sources exceeding about 100 μcuries in activity.

The production of bremsstrahlung when alpha particles strike matter occurs to an extent which, for most purposes, is negligible.

Gamma Radiation

X-rays and gamma rays are essentially the same except for their origin. X-rays come from the electron shells of atoms, whilst gamma rays come from the nuclei of atoms. Their energies are both measured in kiloelectron or megaelectron volts. According to the quantum theory of radiation, a gamma ray travels as a small "packet" of energy known as a photon. 1 MeV gamma rays consist of photons which each have an energy of 1 MeV. The energy of a photon is equal to Planck's constant multiplied by the frequency of the radiation.

Gamma radiation interacts with matter in a rather different way from that in which charged particles interact with it. It cannot be slowed down in matter, since it consists of electromagnetic radiation which travels with the velocity of light. Gamma radiation is absorbed by three main processes.

1. *The Photoelectric Effect*

The whole of the energy of a gamma ray can be used to eject an electron from an atom. The ejected electron then behaves like a beta particle, losing energy until it becomes part of the matter through which it is passing. The photoelectric effect is most important at low gamma-ray energies and increases as the fifth power of the atomic number.

2. *Compton Scattering*

In Compton scattering a gamma ray gives up a portion of its energy to an electron in a material and a gamma ray of reduced energy remains. The latter may escape or it may undergo further Compton scattering. The direction of travel of the gamma ray of reduced energy is different from that of the incident gamma ray.

3. *Pair Production*

Pair production occurs when the energy of a gamma ray is used to create a positron–electron pair. A gamma ray energy of at least $1 \cdot 02$ MeV is required for the formation of a positron–electron pair, but the probability of pair production increases with the energy of the radiation.

Each of these processes reduces the intensity of a beam of gamma radiation, but theoretically it is impossible to reduce the intensity to zero. The reduction in the intensity of a beam of gamma radiation of intensity I by a thickness of absorber dx is proportional to I. Thus one can write

$$\frac{dI}{dx} = -\mu I,$$

where μ is a constant known as the absorption coefficient of the material for gamma radiation of the energy concerned.

$$\frac{dI}{I} = -\mu \, dx.$$

Hence, by integration, $\log_e I = -\mu x + C$, where C is the constant of integration. When $x = 0$, I is equal to the incident intensity I_0. Thus $C = \log_e I_0$.

Therefore $$\log_e \frac{I}{I_0} = -\mu x \qquad (1.5)$$

or $$I = I_0 e^{-\mu x} \qquad (1.6)$$

Thus the equation for the absorption of gamma radiation is of exactly the same form as that for the exponential decay of a radioisotope [see eqn. (1.3)].

The thickness of absorber $x_{\frac{1}{2}}$, which will reduce the intensity of a beam of gamma rays to one-half of its initial intensity, is sometimes required. If one puts $I/I_0 = \frac{1}{2}$ in eqn. (1.6), one finds that $x_{\frac{1}{2}} = 0 \cdot 693/\mu$.

The total absorption coefficient μ is equal to the sum of the partial absorption coefficients due to the photoelectric effect, the Compton scattering and the pair production effect.

In a broad beam of gamma radiation which is striking a large absorbing material, the measured intensity at any point will be greater than that to be expected from the absorption coefficient. This is because photons which have undergone Compton scattering in various parts of the absorber add to the beam intensity. If this effect is appreciable, eqn. (1.6) is modified to take into account the build-up factor B due to the scattering. The modified equation is

$$I/I_0 = Be^{-\mu x}.$$

Isotope Production

Radioisotopes are produced only when atoms undergo nuclear reactions in fairly complicated apparatus. Moderately large quantities of radioisotopes are easily produced in an atomic pile. Inside such a pile (or reactor) there is a flux of perhaps 10^{12} neutrons/cm^2/sec. An atom of an element placed in a pile will often undergo a reaction in which a neutron is absorbed and a gamma ray is emitted. This type of reaction is referred to as an (n, γ) reaction. For example,

$$^{59}\text{Co} + {}_0^1\text{n} \longrightarrow {}^{60}\text{Co} + \gamma.$$

Radioactive cobalt is thus produced from inactive cobalt. Other radioisotopes, such as cerium-144, are produced when uranium atoms are placed in a pile and undergo fission when struck by a neutron.

The radioisotopes produced in an atomic pile are the neutron-rich ones which are usually negative beta emitters, although some alpha emitters are also formed. Proton-rich isotopes, such as sodium-22, are usually made in a cyclotron by bombarding an inactive element with high-energy protons or deuterons. Only one sample can be prepared in a cyclotron at any one time, whereas many specimens of radioactive material can be produced simultaneously in an atomic pile. Proton-rich isotopes are therefore usually much more expensive than neutron-rich pile-produced isotopes. Pile-produced isotopes are much more commonly used.

CHAPTER 2

The Measurement of Nuclear Radiation

NUCLEAR radiation is normally detected and measured by means of the ions created when it passes through matter. If a charged electroscope (such as a gold-leaf electroscope) is put in a radiation field, the ions produced will be attracted to the oppositely charged electrode and the electroscope will gradually be discharged. For any specified type of radiation the rate of discharge is proportional to the intensity of the radiation field.

In ionisation chamber instruments for monitoring radiation fields, a potential is applied between two plates in a gas and the current which passes between them is amplified and indicated on a meter. The meter deflection is proportional to the radiation intensity. Such instruments do not detect individual particles, but merely give an indication of the intensity of the radiation when a large number of particles are passing through the gas.

Geiger Counters

The well-known Geiger–Müller counter (often referred to as a Geiger counter) offers a means of detecting individual particles of nuclear radiation with simple electronic equipment. It is undoubtedly the most suitable detector for use in elementary educational applications.

The Geiger tube consists of a central wire anode with a cylindrical cathode (Fig. 2.1), the space between the electrodes being filled with a suitable gas mixture. The diameter of the cathode is usually a few centimetres. The potential applied between the electrodes depends on the geometry and on the nature of the

16

gas filling, but is usually between 400 and 1600 V. As indicated in Fig. 2.1, the lines of electric intensity are much closer together near the central anode wire than near the cathode. Thus the electric field (in volts per centimetre) near the surface of the anode is much greater than it is near to the cathode.

When a particle of nuclear radiation enters the gas, the electrons formed by the ionisation process travel towards the central wire and the positive ions travel very much more slowly towards the cathode. When the electrons are very near to the surface of the anode wire, the potential gradient is great enough to give them sufficient energy to ionise further molecules of the gas. The

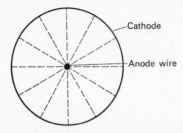

Fig. 2.1. A Geiger tube showing the lines broken of electric intensity.

electrons thus produced are attracted to the anode and ionise further molecules of gas. As this process of gas amplification proceeds, the discharge spreads along the whole length of the anode wire. The total charge which flows through the tube may be as much as 10^8 times the charge of the ions initially produced by the ionising radiation. Geiger tubes therefore produce large output pulses and this usually eliminates the need for a separate amplifier.

The type of circuit in which a Geiger tube is used is shown in Fig. 2.2. Each particle detected by the tube causes a pulse of current to flow through the resistor R so that the Geiger tube anode potential falls by an amount which is usually of the order of 1–10 V. The size of the output pulse is independent of the energy of the radiation, but increases with the applied voltage. This change of potential is fed to the grid of the valve V_1 via the capacitor *C*. The output pulses from V_1 may be used to produce "clicks" in a loud speaker, but they will usually be fed into a piece of electronic equipment which automatically counts them. The value of *R* in Fig. 2.2 is typically 5–10 MΩ and *C* may be about 200 pF.

The fast-moving electrons in a Geiger tube are collected at the central anode wire in a time of the order of a microsecond, but the sheath of the relatively heavy positive ions formed around the anode wire moves much more slowly towards the cathode.

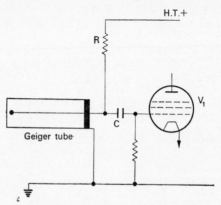

FIG. 2.2. A basic circuit for a Geiger tube.

This sheath of positive ions reduces the potential gradient immediately around the anode wire and prevents a further discharge from occurring for a short time after a particle has been counted. Thus there is a "dead" time of the order of 100 μsec after each count has occurred.

When the positive ions reach the cathode they can cause electrons to be emitted from it. If appropriate precautions are not taken, these electrons will create spurious counts. One way in which such spurious discharges can be "quenched" involves the use of an electronic circuit which will lower the potential applied to the anode of the Geiger tube for a short time immediately following a count. All modern Geiger tubes are, however, self-quenching; that is, a gas is added which will prevent spurious discharges from being initiated when the positive ions reach the cathode.

A Geiger tube is filled with a mixture of inert gases at a pressure of about $0 \cdot 1$ atm. In organically quenched tubes a polyatomic quenching vapour (often ethyl formate) is added. As the positive ion sheath moves towards the cathode, the ions take electrons from the molecules of the quenching gas. The energy possessed by the quenching gas is distributed throughout the molecule and may break a chemical bond. When the organic ions eventually arrive at the cathode, they disintegrate instead of causing electrons to be emitted.

Halogen quenched tubes normally contain a small amount of bromine vapour. The positive ions give up energy to the bromine molecules which may be split into bromine atoms. Halogen quenched tubes have the advantage that they can be designed to operate at potentials of about 400–700 V, whereas organically quenched tubes must have a potential of about 1100–1600 V applied to them. In organically quenched tubes the molecules of the quenching agent are gradually destroyed as the tube is used so that the life of these tubes is normally limited to about 10^{10} counts. In halogen tubes, however, any dissociated bromine molecules will re-unite to re-form the quenching agent; the life of such tubes is almost unlimited. Organically quenched tubes can be permanently damaged by the application of an excessive potential or a potential of reversed polarity, but halogen quenched tubes are not normally affected for more than an hour or so by such treatment. The output pulses provided by halogen quenched tubes are usually larger than those provided by organically quenched tubes. Halogen quenched tubes are therefore generally more suitable for economical student counting equipment.

Geiger Tube Plateau

As the potential applied to a Geiger tube is increased, the amount of gas amplification (and therefore the amplitude of the output pulses) increases. If the applied potential is less than a value known as the starting voltage (V_s in Fig. 2.3), the output pulses will not be large enough to be detected by normal equipment. If the number of particles entering the tube per second is kept constant, the number of counts recorded per unit time increases as the applied voltage is increased above V_s. At applied potentials between V_T and V_c on the plateau of the curve, an increase of potential produces larger output pulses, but only increases the counting rate slightly. At potentials above V_c an

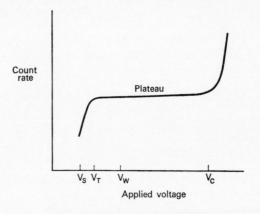

FIG. 2.3. A Geiger tube plateau.

almost continuous discharge occurs; operation in this region for more than a short time will permanently damage an organically quenched tube.

A suitable working point V_w is chosen on the plateau of the curve. In the case of organically quenched tubes the working voltage should not be higher than is necessary, as the greater the working voltage the greater the number of atoms of the quenching agent destroyed per pulse and the shorter the tube life. The working voltage should, however, be well along the plateau so that any small variations of the voltage applied to the Geiger tube will leave the counting rate almost unaffected. The working point of an organically quenched tube is typically chosen as 80 V above the plateau threshold voltage V_T, whereas that for a halogen quenched tube may be chosen as 40 V above V_T since the plateau is often shorter.

It is desirable that a Geiger tube should have a plateau which is almost horizontal and which is fairly long. The slope of the plateau should normally be less than about 0.05% per volt for an organically quenched tube or 0.1% per volt for a halogen quenched tube. The length of the plateau is typically about 200 V, but in some halogen quenched tubes it may be as low as 100 V. Although these figures suggest at first sight that organically quenched tubes have the better characteristics, the halogen quenched tubes operate at a much lower voltage; the effect of a certain percentage change in this voltage is no greater in the case of a halogen quenched tube than it is for an organically quenched tube.

The slight slope of the plateau is due to two main factors, namely an increase in the sensitive volume of the gas filling and an increase in the number of spurious counts with the applied potential.

In some tubes with a thin end window, the threshold voltage for alpha particle detection is some 10–15 V below that for beta detection owing to the larger number of ions produced inside a Geiger tube by an alpha particle. It is therefore possible to operate some tubes between the two threshold potentials so that they will detect alpha but not beta particles. This is not, however, very good practice.

If a Geiger counter is counting at a high rate and the radiation field is suddenly reduced by a large factor, it may take a little time before the tube counts satisfactorily at the low rate. This phenomenon is known as hysteresis and is believed to be due to spurious counts being initiated by excited atoms. If it is necessary to change from a very high counting rate to a much lower rate, it is very desirable to wait for a few minutes, if possible, before taking measurements at the lower rate. The effect is normally very small unless the counting speed at the higher rate is quite large.

Types of Geiger Tube

Geiger tubes may be obtained in many forms. If they are to be used for gamma counting only, the tube may be completely enclosed in metal. The end-window tube shown in Fig. 2.4 is one of the most commonly used types of Geiger tube. The end-window may consist of a thin sheet of aluminium (about 7 mg/cm² in thickness) which allows most types of beta particle to be counted. Only about 10 % of the weak beta particles from carbon-14 (0·15 MeV max.) pass through a window of this thickness. Tubes of a similar design can be made with thin mica end windows

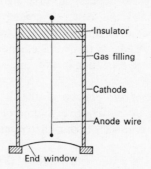

FIG. 2.4. An end-window Geiger tube.

of about 2 mg/cm² and are much more satisfactory for low energy beta particle counting. Some forms of Geiger tube (e.g. the end-window MX168) (Plate A) can be plugged into a socket like a valve and are very useful for simple student equipment. Other types, such as that shown in Fig. 2.4, are intended to be mounted in a lead "castle" (Plate B). If a Geiger tube is surrounded with lead, the number of spurious counts due to stray radioactive atoms is minimised.

Geiger tubes count between about 95 and 100 % of the beta particles which pass into the gas filling. Mica thin end-window tubes can be used to detect alpha particles, but the particles lose a considerable fraction of their energy in passing through the mica window. Where possible alpha particles should be counted with another form of detector which can employ a much thinner window. Only about 1% of gamma photons which strike a Geiger tube are detected. Most gamma photons pass straight through the tube without interacting with it in any way whatsoever, but about 1% of them cause an electron to be emitted from the wall of the tube; it is these electrons rather than the photons themselves which initiate ionisation in the tube.

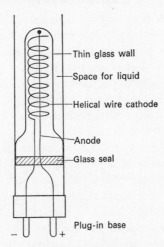

FIG. 2.5. A liquid sample Geiger tube.

Liquid sample tubes are very useful for measuring the activity of a liquid, but they will not detect alpha or weak beta radiation. Some types, such as that shown in Fig. 2.5, will plug into the same type of socket as the MX168 end-window tube and are therefore very useful for school equipment. They usually have a sample volume of 5 ml and a wall thickness of 15 mg/cm². Other types of liquid sample tube (Plate C), for example the MX124/01, are designed for use in a lead castle. The sample volume is 10 ml and the wall thickness about 30 mg/cm². This type of tube is more sensitive than the 5 ml types and normally has somewhat better characteristics. The efficiency of a liquid sample tube is of the order of 2 % for beta particles of a moderately high energy, but is much less than this for low energy beta particles.

Other types of Geiger tube (such as liquid flow tubes and low background tubes) are available, but it is very doubtful whether their use can be justified in a general elementary course.

Scintillation Detectors

Nuclear radiation may be detected by the scintillations (or weak flashes of light) which it produces when it strikes a suitable phosphor. The phosphor converts the energy of the radiation into light. The flashes caused by alpha particles striking an activated zinc sulphide screen may be counted visually by an observer in a darkened room. Although this process is extremely tedious, it was used by Rutherford and others to carry out much of the early work on atomic structure.

In any modern scintillation counter the flashes of light are detected by means of a photomultiplier tube. The light causes electrons to be emitted from the photocathode of the tube and the number of electrons is amplified by secondary emission inside the tube. An output pulse of a fraction of a volt is therefore obtained at the anode of the tube each time a scintillation occurs. The output pulses are fed into an electronic circuit which counts them automatically.

Scintillation detectors provide output pulses which have an amplitude which is proportional to the energy of the incident particles. They are therefore extremely useful when particles of a particular energy range are to be counted since the effect of other particles can be eliminated.

Scintillation counting systems tend to be considerably more expensive than Geiger counting equipment. The experiments described in this book have been selected so that they can be carried out with Geiger counting equipment, since it is doubtful whether the cost of scintillation counting equipment can be justified for work at school level. A gamma scintillation detector can be made with a much higher efficiency than any Geiger system.

Semiconductor Detectors

Semiconductor detectors (Plate D) have become quite important during the last few years.[1, 2, 3] In this type of detector ions are formed in a semiconductor material by the radiation passing through it. The ions are collected by an applied electric field and a pulse is thus obtained. The pulses may be counted electronically.

The semiconductor material used must have a very high resistivity or statistical variations in the current passing will give rise to relatively large "noise" pulses. In addition the material must have relatively few places where ions can be trapped. No known semiconductor material possesses the properties which would enable a homogeneous block of the material to be used as a detector at room temperature. The most convenient forms of detector consist of a *PN* junction. In the region of the junction itself there are very few charge carriers and therefore the resistivity is great enough for this part of the device to be used as a solid state detector. One of the main disadvantages of this form of detector is the limited size of the sensitive volume; this applies especially to the economical forms of detector designed mainly for educational purposes. In addition the output pulses from a semiconductor detector are of much smaller amplitude (typically 1 mV) than those from a Geiger tube. An amplifier must therefore be employed between the detector and the scaler. Semiconductor detectors are especially useful for alpha detection since they can be made with a very thin window and an alpha particle will produce more ions in the sensitive volume than a beta particle or gamma photon.

Scalers

A piece of electronic equipment for counting pulses and indicating the number of pulses counted is known as a scaler (Plate E). This name, incidentally, was originally given to valve circuits which divided or "scaled down" the incoming pulse rate by a known factor so that the output pulses were sufficiently spaced in time for them to be counted by a simple electro-magnetic register.

One of the most economical types of scaler consists of two gas-filled decade tubes followed by an electro-magnetic register. The gas-filled decade tubes can count at a rate of about 4000 pulses/sec. The first tube divides the incoming pulse rate by a factor of 10 and indicates the number of units recorded by means of a red glow in the gas. At each tenth input pulse from the Geiger tube a pulse is fed from the first (or units) decade tube to the second tube which indicates the number of tens. At each hundredth pulse from the Geiger tube, a pulse is fed from the second decade tube to the electro-magnetic register. Although a typical electro-magnetic register can count at speeds not exceeding about 20 pulses/sec, it can indicate four or more digits. Decade tubes of the gas-filled type are often called "Dekatrons", but this term should really be reserved for the tubes manufactured by Ericsson Telephones Ltd., since it is a trade mark of this company. A number of manufacturers have commenced to produce economical scalers during the last few years to meet the increasing demand for relatively inexpensive educational equipment; most of them have a built-in power supply for the Geiger tube.

Statistics of Counting

The time at which a given nucleus will decay does not depend on its previous history or on the decay of neighbouring atoms. There is merely a certain probability that it will decay within a specified time. The counting rate in any experiment with radio-isotopes therefore shows random fluctuations about a mean value. These fluctuations are governed by the laws of statistics.

The standard deviation or standard error is normally used as a measure of the statistical error in a number of counts. It is equal to the square root of the mean number of counts which would be obtained from many observations made over the same time interval. In radioisotope work the mean number of counts is not normally known, but the standard deviation is approximately equal to the square root of the number of counts recorded provided that the latter is not small.

It can be shown from the theory of statistics that there is a chance of $31 \cdot 7\%$ (or about 1 in 3) of the error in a number of counts exceeding the standard deviation and a chance of $4 \cdot 6\%$ (or about 1 in 20) of the error exceeding twice the standard deviation. If 10^6 counts are recorded, the standard deviation is about 1000. Thus there is a chance of about 1 in 3 that the error will exceed a 1000 or $0 \cdot 1\%$ and a chance of less than 1 in 20 that it will exceed 2000 or $0 \cdot 2\%$. If 10,000 counts are recorded there is a chance of about 1 in 3 that the error will exceed 100 or 1%, whilst if only 100 counts are recorded, there is a chance of about 1 in 3 that the error will exceed 10%. Thus the standard deviation increases as the square root of the number of counts, but the percentage error is inversely proportional to the square root of the number of counts.

In a typical student experiment some 10,000 counts may be obtained. Thus an accuracy of better than $\pm 1\%$ cannot normally be expected. Only 27 counts in 10,000 have a deviation greater than 3 times the standard deviation. It is therefore reasonable to reject any counts which show a deviation from the mean greater than 3 times the standard deviation.

It may be found that the deviations of the number of counts are considerably greater than would be expected from the theory. This is an indication that the equipment is not functioning normally. For example, a drift in the potential applied to the Geiger tube may increase the spread in the count rates obtained. One should not suspect the equipment, however, unless the departure from the theory is quite appreciable.

Resolving Time

If two ionising particles pass into a Geiger counter or any other form of detector within a certain time of one another, they will be counted as one particle. The limiting time is known as the resolving time of the system. A typical Geiger counter has a resolving time of the order of 100 μsec, this being determined mainly by the speed of travel of the positive ions to the cathode. A scintillation counter has a much smaller resolving time and can therefore count at a much higher speed. In addition the electronic equipment to which the pulses from the Geiger tube are fed will have its own resolving time, since it cannot count two pulses separately if they are spaced very close together in time.

In most of the economical student equipment intended for elementary work in schools and colleges no allowance is made for lost counts due to the resolving time of the equipment. The resolving time of a Geiger tube is in any case rather indeterminate and varies with age. If, therefore, it is desired to correct for the lost counts due to the resolving time of the equipment, the Geiger tube is connected to an electronic circuit which has a longer resolving time than that of the tube, but one which is accurately known. The resolving time of the whole equipment then becomes equal to the resolving time of the electronic circuit. The circuit normally takes the form of a "quenching probe unit" which is placed between the Geiger tube and the scaler and which reduces the potential at the Geiger tube anode below the threshold voltage for a time equal to the resolving time.

Resolving Time Corrections

The number of counts which are not recorded because the resolving time is not zero may be calculated in the following way. If the resolving time is τ sec and there are n counts/sec, the total time per second during which the system is inactive is $n\tau$ sec. Thus the time for which the equipment is sensitive during any one second period of the count is $(1 - n\tau)$ sec. The corrected counting rate = no. of counts/time = $n/(1 - n\tau)$. The correction is negligible at low counting rates. In a typical counting apparatus the resolving time may be set at 400 μsec, in which case the correction amounts to 10% of the number of counts recorded at a counting rate of 13,600 counts/min.

If a set of recorded counts is to be corrected for the losses due to the finite resolving time, the correction is most conveniently carried out by the use of a table (Appendix 3) showing the number of counts per minute recorded and the number of lost counts which must be added to the recorded counting rate. A separate table is required for each value of the resolving time. Most British laboratories tend to set their equipment for a 400 μsec resolving time. In elementary educational experiments the correction is often neglected.

Background Counts

A Geiger tube or any other form of radiation detector will register some counts even when no radioactive material is near to it. Stray radioactive atoms are always present in the air and cosmic rays are entering the earth's atmosphere from space; these give rise to the background counting rate. This background counting rate should be subtracted from the measured counting rate. If a correction is made for lost counts due to the finite resolving time of the system, this correction should be made before the background counting rate is subtracted.

It can be shown that the standard deviation of the net sample counting rate σ_s is related to the standard deviation of the total counting rate (sample plus background) σ_T and that of the background σ_b by the following equation:

$$\sigma_s = \sqrt{(\sigma_T{}^2 + \sigma_b{}^2)} \qquad (2.1)$$

If n_T is the number of sample plus background counts recorded in a time t_T, R_T is the counting rate of the sample plus background, R_b is the background counting rate (recorded over a time t_b):

$$\sigma_T = \frac{\sqrt{n_T}}{t_T} = \frac{\sqrt{(R_T t_T)}}{t_T} = \sqrt{\left(\frac{R_T}{t_T}\right)}.$$

Similarly, $$\sigma_b = \sqrt{\left(\frac{R_b}{t_b}\right)}.$$

Thus $$\sigma_s = \sqrt{\left(\frac{R_T}{t_T} + \frac{R_b}{t_b}\right)}.$$

If one considers the case where $t_T + t_b$ is constant and differen tiates the above equation, by putting $d\sigma_s = 0$ one obtains th following condition for minimum σ_s when the total countin time is specified:

$$\frac{t_T}{t_b} = \sqrt{\left(\frac{R_T}{R_b}\right)}.$$

Thus if the sample plus background counting rate is similar t the background rate alone, the time spent determining the back ground rate should be about the same as that spent countin the sample. If, however, the sample counting rate is 100 or mor times the background counting rate, the time spent on th determination of the latter may be quite small.

Ratemeters

Ratemeters (Plates F and G) do not count each individual puls received from a Geiger tube or other detector, but merely indicat the average pulse rate as a deflection of a meter. The accurac with which the average pulse rate can be found is obvious greater with a scaler than with a ratemeter, but, neverthele ratemeters are often useful in lecture demonstrations and fo monitoring where a continuous indication of the counting rat is required rather than an accurate measurement involving timing operation.

Ratemeters, like scalers, show statistical fluctuations in th counting rate. Essentially each pulse from a Geiger tube cause a small amount of charge to be fed to a capacitor C in parall with a resistor R; the ratemeter reading is proportional to th voltage across the RC combination. If the product of R and (the time constant) is large, the ratemeter will smooth out fluctuations in the counting rate which occur over a reasonably long period of time, but the time to reach the final reading will be longer than if a small time constant is selected. When pulses are first fed to the ratemeter input, the meter reading will gradually rise as the potential across C increases until it differs from the asympototic final reading by a negligible amount. A time of $2\cdot3\ RC$ sec is required for the reading to reach 90% of its asymptotic final value or $4\cdot6\ RC$ sec for it to reach 99% of its final value. If a time constant of 40 sec is selected, one should, therefore, wait for at least 3 min before taking a reading if 1% accuracy is desired. Such a long time-constant is only required when the counting rate is low, since the ratemeter must then smooth out the relatively large statistical variations in the counting rate. A single reading on a ratemeter has the same standard deviation as would be obtained by counting for a time $2\ RC$ sec with a scaler where RC is the ratemeter time constant. The error can naturally be reduced by taking a series of readings. The time constant is normally selected by trial and error so that the smallest value which provides a steady reading can be used.

Absolute and Relative Counting

If a source emitting a certain number of particles per second is placed beneath the end window of a Geiger tube, the counting rate will be much less than the rate of emission of the particles. Some of the particles will not be counted simply because they are emitted in a direction other than towards the window of the Geiger tube. Others will be absorbed even before they can escape from the source itself ("self-absorption"), whilst some particles will be absorbed in the Geiger tube window or in the air between the source and the window. Yet another complicating factor is the reflection of particles from the material on which the source is mounted ("back scattering").

These factors render the accurate absolute measurement of source strength by means of an end-window counter rather difficult. Fortunately, however, it is not usually necessary to measure absolute counting rates. Geiger counting equipment is normally used to measure changes in disintegration rates with time or to compare the activities of various samples. It is therefore only necessary to provide a reproducible geometry.

Absorption Measurements

It is often necessary to estimate the energy of beta radiation in order to identify the emitting isotope. Beta radiation consists of particles of energies varying from zero up to a certain maximum value which is characteristic of the nuclide concerned. Beta energies are normally expressed in terms of the maximum energy of the particles or of the range of the particles in milligrammes per square centimetre in aluminium. Unfortunately, the maximum range is not especially easy to measure accurately.

If an end-window tube is used to count the particles from a beta emitter and absorbers are placed between the source and the window, a graph of $\log_{10}$ (counting rate) against the absorber thickness is fairly linear over the greater part of its length. This linearity is purely fortuitous. It so happens that the energy distribution of the radiation combined with scattering in the absorber, etc., lead to an approximately exponential absorption. The eqns. (1.5) and (1.6) can thus be applied empirically to beta absorption, μ being the absorption coefficient.

The almost horizontal portion of the absorption curve shown in Fig. 2.6 is due to the so-called bremsstrahlung. This form of electro-magnetic radiation is produced by the slowing down of beta particles in the absorber in much the same way as X-rays are produced by the slowing down of electrons in an X-ray tube. The number of counts due to the bremsstrahlung is only a very small fraction of the total beta counting rate. In the case of a beta/gamma emitter, however, the horizontal portion of the curve will occur at a much higher counting rate.

An approximate estimation of a maximum beta ray energy may be made by the "half-thickness" method. The thickness of absorber required to reduce the counting rate to one-half of its value when no absorber was present is found. The maximum energy of the beta radiation may be estimated from a graph of energy against half-thickness or by use of the following approximate equation:

$$x_{\frac{1}{2}} = 46E^{3/2},$$

where $x_{\frac{1}{2}}$ is the value of the half-thickness in milligrammes per square centimetre and E is the energy of the beta radiation in megaelectron volts.

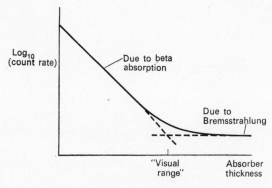

FIG. 2.6. A typical beta absorption curve.

The energy may also be determined if an estimate can be made of the thickness of the absorber required to remove all of the beta particles. The maximum range of the beta particles is not, however, very easy to measure from the normal absorption curve shown in Fig. 2.6, since it involves estimating the point at which the extrapolated bremsstrahlung curve meets the extrapolated absorption curve. These extrapolated sections are shown dotted in Fig. 2.6. The range at the point where they meet is often referred to as the "visual range"; it is generally smaller than the actual maximum range. The process of estimating the visual range may be almost impossible if any gamma radiation is present. In the case of a pure beta emitter the maximum range is sometimes assumed to be the absorber thickness which will reduce the counting rate by a factor of 10,000.

A better estimate of the maximum beta particle range can be made by the Feather method.[4, 5, 6] In this case the absorption curve is compared with that obtained using a standard beta emitter of known range. The absorption curve for the standard source is divided into 10 equal parts along the range axis. The fractional transmission of the particles from the standard source

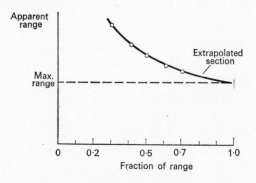

FIG. 2.7. A Feather plot.

is found at each of these points. The absorber thicknesses required to reduce the unknown sample counting rate by the same factors is found graphically. These are assumed to correspond to absorber thicknesses of $0·1$, $0·2$, $0·3$, $0·4$, etc., times the maximum range of the particles from the unknown source. The apparent range of the particles from the unknown source is found for each of these tenth thicknesses and plotted on another graph against the appropriate tenth factor (Fig. 2.7). The value of the maximum range is taken to be the extrapolated point on this graph at an absorber thickness equal to the full range.

The maximum energy of the beta particles may be found from a graph of maximum beta particle energy against maximum range.

Alternatively it may be found (with somewhat less accuracy) from one of the following expressions:

$$\left. \begin{array}{l} E = 1\cdot85R + 0\cdot245 \text{ MeV} \quad \text{for } R > 0\cdot3 \text{ g/cm}^2, \\ E = 1\cdot92R^{0\cdot725} \quad \text{for } R < 0\cdot3 \text{ g/cm}^2, \end{array} \right\} \quad (2.2)$$

where E is the maximum beta particle energy in megaelectron volts and R is the maximum range in grammes per square centimetre.

Beta absorption curves are almost independent of the material used in the absorber provided that the absorber thicknesses are

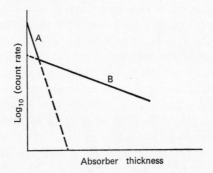

Fig. 2.8. A beta absorption curve containing two components.

expressed in grammes per square centimetre. For example, the maximum range of certain beta particles in aluminium is $0\cdot4$ g/cm^2, whereas in copper it is $0\cdot5$ g/cm^2. The difference is mainly due to the slightly smaller number of electrons present in a certain weight of copper than in the same weight of aluminium. Gamma radiation is, however, absorbed much more strongly by material of high atomic number. Aluminium absorbers are usually used for beta absorption because they have little effect on gamma radiation, whilst lead absorbers are used in gamma ray absorption experiments. If a beta absorption curve is to be plotted when X-rays or very low-energy gamma rays are being emitted, a set of beryllium absorbers is very useful. This material is of very low atomic number and has little effect on photons.

If a beta source emits two sets of beta particles with widely different ranges, the absorption curve will approximate to two straight lines *A* and *B* in Fig. 2.8. If *B* is extrapolated back, the counting rate at zero absorber thickness may be estimated for this component alone. The energy of the two types of radiation may be estimated from the slopes of the two lines. It must be emphasised, however, that reasonable resolution will be obtained only if the energies of the two components differ by a factor of about two or more.

Gamma ray energies may be estimated in a similar way by absorption measurements using lead absorbers. The absorption coefficient or the half-thickness is found. The absorption will be exponential only if the electrons ejected from the absorbers are not counted and if gamma rays degraded by Compton scattering do not enter the detector. A good approximation to exponential absorption can be attained if an aluminium absorber of about 700 mg/cm² is placed as near as possible to the Geiger tube window and the source is placed 1 or 2 in. away. The lead absorbers should be placed immediately above the source. Some ambiguity may occur if gamma rays of a fairly high energy are present, since the absorption coefficient of lead shows a minimum at about 3 MeV. Thus gamma rays of 2·0 and 6·0 MeV both have half-thicknesses of about 15·5 g/cm².

Self-absorption

When beta counting is performed with a source which is not very thin, the effect of absorption inside the source must normally be considered. (Gamma absorption is usually negligible in a source of the type used for counting.) The correction for this beta self-absorption is usually negligible if the thickness of the sample in milligrammes per square centimetre is less than about 1% of the maximum range of the beta particles.

The self-absorption (or self-weakening) correction factor *s*,

PLATE A. An MX168 Geiger tube in a stand. A plastic guard protects the end window. (Research Electronics Ltd.)

PLATE B. The economical Research Electronics lead castle arranged for counting solid samples. A sealed source is shown in position beneath the lead absorber. This castle, which has been developed for educational use, has the advantage that it can also be used for liquid sample counting.

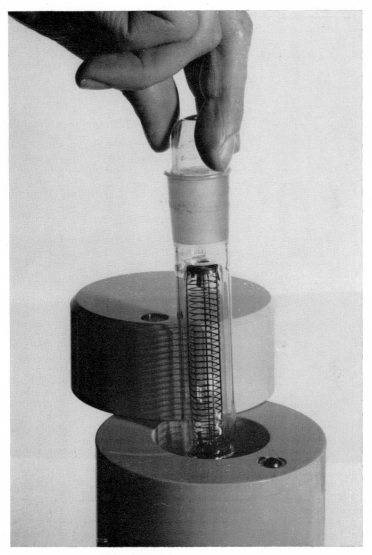

PLATE C. A liquid sample tube being inserted into a lead castle.
(Isotope Developments Ltd.)

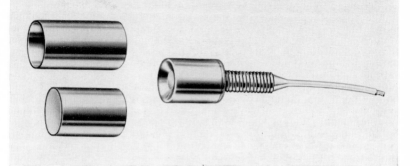

PLATE D. The Twentieth Century Electronics semiconductor detector type SSN/03K (*right*). A push on protective sleeve (*upper left*) and a conversion foil for neutron counting (*lower left*) are also shown.

PLATE E. The Jonpar Electronics Scaler type 628. This is an inexpensive scaler developed mainly for educational use. The first six digits of the number counted are indicated by the magnetic register at the upper left-hand side, the tens digit by the adjacent decade tube and the units digit by the right-hand decade tube.

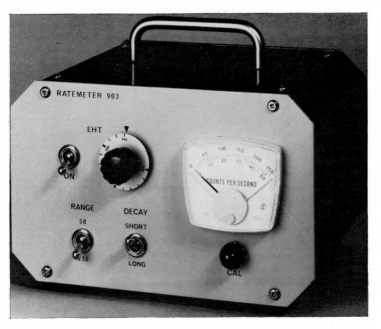

PLATE F. The Research Electronics ratemeter type 903. It is an economical instrument intended for educational purposes.

PLATE G. The Panax Equipment ratemeter type RM202 (*left*) and the Panax scaler type 102ST (*right*).

PLATE H. The Griffin and George ionisation chamber instrument. It may be used for the estimation of the half-life of thoron (experiment 7.12) and for other experiments.

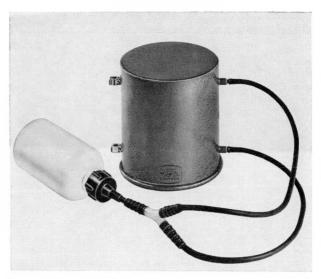

PLATE I. The Griffin and George thoron source and ionisation chamber. When the plastic bottle, which contains 25 g of thorium hydroxide, is squeezed, air containing the thoron circulates around the closed system.

Plate J. The Griffin and George pulse electroscope. (Suitable apparatus for mounting this electroscope and for projecting an image of the leaf is available from the manufacturers.)

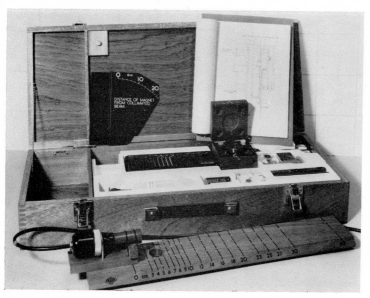

Plate K. The Panax Equipment kit SK107B for educational use. This contains a set of sources, an instruction book and all of the apparatus required to carry out simple experiments except for the Geiger tube and the scaler or ratemeter.

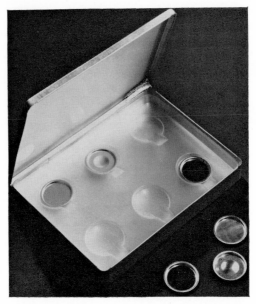

PLATE L. A box for carrying or storing planchets. (Nucleonic Accessories Ltd.)

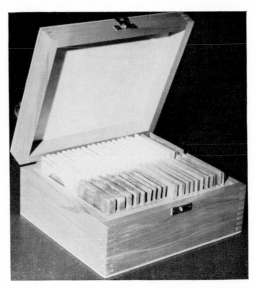

PLATE M. A complete set of aluminium and lead absorbers. (Nucleonic Accessories Ltd.)

is defined as the factor by which an observed counting rate must be divided in order to find the counting rate which would have been obtained if no self-absorption had taken place.

Let t = source thickness (mg/cm²), n' = count rate which would have been obtained without self-absorption, n = observed counting rate, μ = coefficient of beta absorption [see eqns. (1.5) and (1.6)].

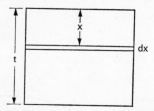

FIG. 2.9. Self-absorption in a source of thickness t.

Consider a section of the source of thickness dx mg/cm² at a distance x mg/cm² from the upper surface of the source (Fig. 2.9). If no self-absorption were present, this section alone would give rise to a counting rate of

$$dn' = n' \frac{dx}{t}.$$

In fact, however, the counting rate from this source is reduced by a factor of $e^{-\mu x}$ owing to the absorption in the layers of material above it. Hence the counting rate dn due to this thin layer is

$$dn = n' \frac{dx}{t} e^{-\mu x}$$

$$n = \int dn = \int_0^t n' \frac{dx}{t} e^{-\mu x} = \frac{n'}{t} \int_0^t e^{-\mu x} dx$$

$$n = \frac{n'}{t} \left[\frac{-e^{-\mu x}}{\mu} \right]_0^t = \frac{n'}{\mu t} (1 - e^{-\mu t}).$$

Thus

$$s = \frac{n}{n'} = \frac{1}{\mu t} (1 - e^{-\mu t}). \tag{2.3}$$

This equation is only approximate, since it has been assumed that the absorption is truly exponential. It leads to the familiar "saturation" type of curve shown in Fig. 2.10.

It is obvious that if a sample is made thicker (in mg/cm²) than the maximum range of the particles it emits, any increase in the sample thickness made by adding the same material will not result in an increase of counting rate. The sample is then said to have infinite thickness.

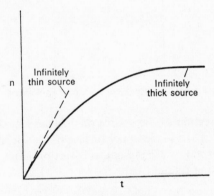

FIG. 2.10. A self-absorption curve.

If a comparison of the total activity of thick samples of a beta emitter is to be made, allowance must be made for self-absorption. If, however, a count rate which is proportional to the specific activity is required, the self-absorption effect may be advantageous. Counts made on materials of the same chemical compound in sources of the same surface area will be proportional to the specific activity (μcuries/g) if the samples are of infinite thickness. The exact amount of material used will not affect the result.

The self-absorption half-thickness ($s = \frac{1}{2}$) is about 2·3 times the half-thickness measured with external absorbers.

In the case of fairly thin sources in which μt is less than about 0·1, the self-absorption may be allowed for by adding half the source thickness in milligrammes per square centimetre to the external absorber thickness. The approximate validity of this assumption can be verified by expanding eqn. (2.3):

$$s = \frac{1}{\mu t}(1 - e^{-\mu t}) \simeq \frac{1}{\mu t}\left\{1 - \left[1 - \mu t + \frac{(\mu t)^2}{2} - \ldots\right]\right\}$$

$$s \simeq 1 - \frac{\mu t}{2} \simeq e^{\frac{-\mu t}{2}}$$

The Pocket Dosimeter

The pocket dosimeter is a small ionisation chamber instrument with a tubular metal body of a size similar to that of a fountain pen. When the instrument is to be read, the appropriate end of it is held to the eye like a telescope so that the scale on an internal graticule can be seen through the microscope system (Fig. 2.11). If the small internal quartz fibre is charged to a suitable potential (about 220 V), the image of it will appear to move across the scale to the zero mark. When a dose of radiation is received, the amount of charge lost will be dependent on the amount of radiation; the latter can be read from the scale at any time.

Pocket dosimeters are not especially sensitive instruments and will not normally record the very low doses received during educational experiments. In some types the reading may change somewhat if a severe mechanical shock is received by the instrument. They are, nevertheless, useful for monitoring people who are likely to receive an appreciable dose in the course of their work. The reading of this type of instrument gradually increases when it is charged, since the insulation cannot be made perfect.

The Quartz Fibre Ionisation Chamber (Plates H and I)

The ionisation chamber inside a pocket dosimeter is very small and consequently the sensitivity is low. In order to increase the sensitivity for school purposes, instruments are being manufactured in which a pocket dosimeter is connected to an ionisation chamber of about 200 ml in volume (Fig. 2.12). The quartz fibre of the dosimeter is connected electrically to the centre probe wire of the ionisation chamber. Under these conditions a fraction of a microcurie of an alpha emitter or a few microcuries of a beta

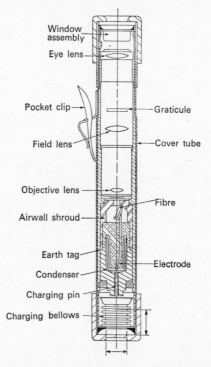

FIG. 2.11. A pocket dosimeter. (R. A. Stephen & Co. Ltd.)

emitter will cause the quartz fibre to move across the scale in a few minutes. The scale readings show only relative magnitudes when the dosimeter is connected to the larger chamber. A light guide is employed so that the instrument can be read without having to be removed from the chamber.

The base of the chamber is removable in order to allow samples to be inserted. Absorbers may also be placed above the sample tray. This type of instrument is most useful for alpha detection, since it has the advantage that there is no window to absorb this type of radiation. In particular, its use in the estimation of the half-life of thoron gas will be discussed in a later chapter. The instrument is not suitable for the measurement of gamma sources of less than about 50 μcuries in activity.

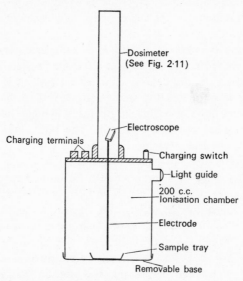

Fig. 2.12. A quartz-fibre ionisation chamber. (Another type is shown in Plate H.)

The instrument should be charged from a high impedance source of variable voltage. A resistor of between 1 and 10 MΩ may be connected in the charging circuit to prevent the possibility of shock. The source of charging potential is connected to the electroscope only when the charging switch button is depressed. This button must therefore be depressed whilst the source of voltage is adjusted for a zero reading of the instrument. If any objects are to be placed inside the chamber, they should be in place before the zero adjustments are made, since their proximity to the probe will affect the capacity of the instrument and hence the reading.

The Pulse Electroscope

Pulse electroscopes (such as the Wulf electroscope) can be used for certain demonstration experiments where a very small current is to be measured, e.g. the current passing between two electrodes in ionised air.

The pulse electroscope (Plate J) is somewhat similar to the gold-leaf electroscope, but has an electrode at the side which is often earthed. As the deflection increases, a point is reached at which the leaf touches the side electrode and is discharged. If more current flows into the leaf, the leaf will again be discharged when it reaches the side electrode. The rate of discharge (or pulsing) of the leaf is proportional to the current flowing. This type of electroscope is usually constructed so that a shadow of the leaf can be thrown onto a screen for an audience to see.

The distance of the side electrode from the leaf can be varied. This will affect the sensitivity, the maximum sensitivity being about 10^{-11} to 10^{-12} A. Before the instrument is used, a potential difference should be applied between the electrodes to check that there is no leakage (which will be indicated as a pulsing of the leaf). If leakage is present, the outside insulator of the instrument should be carefully cleaned.

CHAPTER 3

Naturally Occurring Radioisotopes

THERE are quite a number of naturally occurring isotopes which are somewhat radioactive. Some of these, such as ^{14}C and ^{3}H, are formed in the upper atmosphere by cosmic ray bombardment. The others either have a very long half-life (not less than about 10^8 years) or are formed by the radioactive decay of elements of long half-life. All radionuclides of half-life less than about 10^7 years which were present when the earth was formed will now have decayed so that their activity can no longer be detected.

Natural Radioactive Series

Uranium and thorium containing minerals provide sources of higher specific activity than other naturally occurring radioisotopes. These elements are by no means uncommon. Sea water contains about 2 parts in 10^9 of uranium and it has been estimated that thorium is about 4 times as abundant on the earth as uranium. As the radioactive properties of these elements were investigated, it gradually became clear that three "families" of naturally occurring elements exist. These are shown in Figs. 3.1, 3.2 and 3.3; some further details are given in Appendix 2. It can be seen from Fig. 3.1 that the long-lived parent atom ^{238}U decays radioactively into the fairly short-lived daughter product ^{234}Th (an isotope of ordinary thorium) which decays successively into other elements until the stable ^{206}Pb is reached. Similarly, thorium is the parent atom of the thorium series, whilst the third series, although known as the actinium series, has uranium–235 ("Actinouranium, AcU") as its parent. Natural uranium

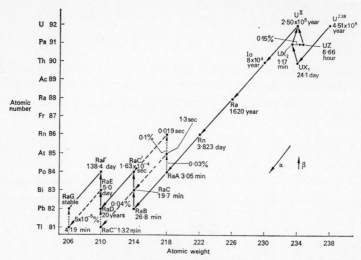

FIG. 3.1. The uranium–radium series.

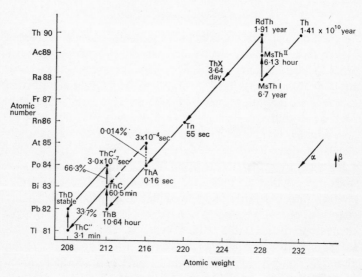

FIG. 3.2. The thorium series.

contains about 0.71% of ^{235}U; it was this isotope which was separated to make some atomic bombs.

When the isotopes of the radioactive series were first named, the actual elements produced in the decay were not known. For example, the elements in a radioactive material separated from uranium were not identified immediately and were given the historical name uranium X. When this material was separated

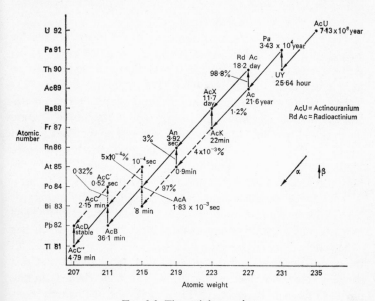

FIG. 3.3. The actinium series.

into the two isotopes ^{234}Th and ^{234m}Pa, these were given the symbols UX$_1$ and UX$_2$ respectively. It was later found that another nuclide of the same atomic weight and the same atomic number as UX$_2$ was present and this was called UZ; its nucleus has a different energy level from that of UX$_2$. These historical names are still often used largely because the use of symbols such as UX$_1$ and RaC immediately make it obvious that the isotopes are in the uranium–radium series and give some idea of the positions they occupy in that series. If, however, one uses the corresponding symbols ^{234m}Pa and ^{214}Bi for these elements, one has to think into which family each element falls. The use of the symbols ^{234m}Pa and ^{214}Bi does, however, make the chemical properties of the element immediately known. In many cases as new isotopes were discovered in the decay chain, historical names such as RaC′ and RaC″ were used, since RaD had already been allocated to an element which had been previously discovered in a later part of the decay chain.

The emission of a beta or gamma particle leaves the atomic weight of a nuclide unchanged, whilst the emission of an alpha particle results in the formation of an isotope which has an atomic weight of 4 units less than that of its parent. Thorium-232 has an atomic weight which is an integral multiple of 4 and therefore all its decay products also have atomic weights which are integral multiples of 4 (any fractions being ignored). The thorium family of elements may therefore be referred to as the 4n series. Similarly, the uranium–radium family may be referred to as the (4n + 2) series and the actinium family as the (4n + 3) series.

It might be expected that a (4n + 1) series would also exist. This is not found in nature, but can be produced artificially. The longest-lived member of the series is neptunium-237 which has a half-life of $2 \cdot 2 \times 10^6$ years. This is very much shorter than the age of the earth and therefore no detectable amounts of this element remain at the present time. The final element in the (4n + 1) series is the stable ^{209}Bi, whereas the other three series end in isotopes of lead.

Radioactive Equilibrium

Let us consider a long-lived parent nuclide such as ^{238}U and its fairly short-lived daughter product ^{234}Th. If one commences with a sample of pure ^{238}U, it will initially emit alpha particles only, but as the amount of ^{234}Th formed by the decay of the ^{238}U increases, beta activity will also be found. The long half-life of the parent $(4 \cdot 51 \times 10^9$ years) ensures that the amount of this material remains constant for all practical purposes over many centuries. The rate of formation of ^{234}Th (which is, according to eqn. (1.1), proportional to the number of atoms of ^{238}U) therefore remains constant. However, the isotope ^{234}Th cannot continue to accumulate for very long owing to its short half-life.

After a year or so the ^{234}Th (half-life $24 \cdot 1$ days) is decaying at almost exactly the same rate as it is being formed from ^{238}U. If λ_1 and λ_2 are the radioactive constants for ^{238}U and ^{234}Th respectively and N_1 and N_2 are the number of atoms of these elements present in the sample, the rate of disintegration of the ^{238}U is $\lambda_1 N_1$ and that of the ^{234}Th is $\lambda_2 N_2$ [see eqn. (1.1)]. At equilibrium when these rates are equal $\lambda_1 N_1 = \lambda_2 N_2$ or

$$\frac{N_2}{N_1} = \frac{\lambda_1}{\lambda_2} = \frac{t_{\frac{1}{2}(2)}}{t_{\frac{1}{2}(1)}}, \tag{3.1}$$

where $t_{\frac{1}{2}(1)}$ and $t_{\frac{1}{2}(2)}$ are the half-lives of ^{238}U and ^{234}Th respectively. Thus the rates of disintegration of each of the isotopes in a decay series is the same at equilibrium provided that the parent atom is much longer lived than any daughter product.

If a specimen of uranium has been isolated in the earth for a very long time, the number of atoms of each of the elements present is proportional to their half-lives. If the half-life of the intermediate elements is much shorter than that of the parent (as is the case in the natural families), the amounts of each of these elements present at equilibrium falls with the half-life of the parent.

The amount of ^{206}Pb in uranium ores is gradually increasing with time and this provides a method for the estimation of the age of the ores or for the age of the earth itself.

Let us consider further the case of a long-lived parent decaying into a short-lived daughter product, taking the case of the decay of ^{238}U to ^{234}Th as an example. It has already been stated that the amount of ^{238}U and hence the rate of formation of ^{234}Th is constant with time over many centuries. Let this rate of formation of ^{234}Th be a atoms/sec in a certain sample which initially consists of pure ^{238}U. The rate of increase in the number of atoms of

^{234}Th is equal to its rate of formation minus its rate of decay, that is

$$\frac{dN_2}{dt} = (a - \lambda_2 N_2), \tag{3.2}$$

where the symbols have the same meaning as previously. Hence

$$\frac{dN_2}{(a - \lambda_2 N_2)} = dt.$$

Integrating,

$$-\frac{1}{\lambda_2} \log_e (a - \lambda_2 N_2) = t + C.$$

As $N_2 = 0$ when $t = 0$, the constant of integration,

$$C = -\frac{1}{\lambda_2} \log_e a.$$

Thus the equation becomes

$$-\frac{1}{\lambda_2} \log_e \left[\frac{1}{a}(a - \lambda_2 N_2) \right] = t$$

or

$$\frac{1}{a} (a - \lambda_2 N_2) = e^{-\lambda_2 t}$$

$$\frac{\lambda_2 N_2}{a} = 1 - e^{-\lambda_2 t}$$

$$N_2 = \frac{a}{\lambda_2} (1 - e^{-\lambda_2 t})$$

or

$$N_2 = K(1 - e^{-\lambda_2 t}) \tag{3.3}$$

where K is a constant. This is the same type of "saturation" curve as that of eqn. (2.3.) (Fig. 2.10).

In 1900 Crookes observed that if excess ammonium carbonate was added to a solution of uranyl nitrate, a minute amount of precipitate remained undissolved. This undissolved material carried almost all of the activity initially present in the uranium; it was called uranium X. Initially this experiment led to the uggestion that the activity of uranium was not a property of uranium itself, but Becquerel found that the activity of the uranium X decayed with a half-life of about 24 days (curve *A* in Fig. 3.4).

Crystals of uranyl nitrate could be obtained from the filtrate obtained in this experiment; they had virtually no activity. It was found that they regained their activity according to eqn. (3.3) (curve *B* of Fig. 3.4). Thus the formation and decay of ^{234}Th can be demonstrated. The total activity remains constant; this can be verified by adding instantaneous values of the activity

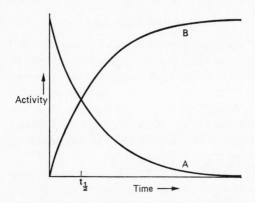

FIG. 3.4. Growth and decay curves of an isotope.

shown in the two curves of Fig. 3.4. In ordinary uranium which has not been chemically treated for a year, the activity of the ^{234}Th is constant since it is formed as rapidly as it decays. A very similar experiment can be carried out to separate thorium X from thorium.

The term "secular equilibrium" is applied to the case of a long-lived parent decaying into a short-lived daughter product. A number of cases of secular equilibrium are found both in the natural radioisotopes (^{234}Th–^{234m}Pa, ^{226}Ra–^{222}Rn, etc.) and in artificially produced isotopes (^{144}Ce–^{144}Pr, ^{137}Cs–^{137m}Ba, etc.).

Branching Chains

It can be seen from Figs. 3.1, 3.2 and 3.3 that certain nuclides in the naturally occurring families disintegrate in more than one way. For example, 99·97% of RaA emits alpha particles forming RaB, whilst 0·03% forms $^{218}_{85}At$. Any sections of the decay schemes which represent less than 1% of the parent activity are shown by dotted arrows. In Fig. 3.1 ^{234}Pa exists in two forms of different nuclear energy. 0·15% of UX_2 changes to UZ before becoming ^{234}U.

Uranium Compounds

Ordinary uranium consists mainly of the isotope ^{238}U, but small quantities of other isotopes of the element are also present. Normal uranium compounds, as purchased from most British chemical suppliers, consist of the appropriate compound of "depleted" uranium which has been supplied by the United Kingdom Atomic Energy Authority. Depleted uranium contains about 0·41% of ^{235}U, 0·02% of ^{236}U and 0·003% of ^{234}U, whereas natural uranium contains about 0·711% of ^{235}U, 0·006% of ^{234}U and no ^{236}U. A few uranium compounds of natural isotopic composition are available from chemical suppliers, but they are considerably more expensive than similar compounds of the depleted material. Any of the experiments to be described which require a uranium compound may be carried out using the depleted material.

Uranium compounds as purchased will probably contain ^{234}Th in radioactive equlibrium with the ^{238}U, but if equilibrium has not been reached, it will only be necessary to keep the compound for about 9 months for a constant activity to be attained [see eqn. (3.3)]. ^{234m}Pa will be in equilibrium with the ^{234}Th and with the ^{238}U if the ^{234}Th is in equilibrium with the latter. Depleted uranium contains a smaller amount of ^{234}U than the natural product; however, there is no possibility of equilibrium being attained, since ^{234}U has a half-life of about 250,000 years. Ionium

(^{230}Th) will be removed during the manufacture of uranium compounds. Although some ^{234}U will decay to ionium, the activity of the latter will be negligible, since it has a half-life of 80,000 years. None of the elements following ionium in the uranium series (Fig. 3.1) will be present in detectable amounts in commercial uranium compounds, since the long half-lives of ^{234}U and ionium effectively constitute a break in the chain.

Even in uranium of natural isotopic composition, only $0 \cdot 71 \%$ of ^{235}U is present. However, this has a shorter half-life than ^{238}U and its activity will be about $4 \cdot 5 \%$ of the ^{238}U activity in a uranium compound of natural isotopic composition. UY (^{231}Th) will be in equilibrium with ^{235}U, since it has a half-life of $25 \cdot 64$ hr, but ^{231}Pa will not reach equilibrium, since its half-life is $3 \cdot 43 \times 10^4$ years. The activity of ^{231}Pa in a sample of a uranium compound and the activity of the following decay products will therefore be negligible.

In a sample of a uranium compound the only activities which need be considered are those due to ^{238}U, ^{234}Th, ^{234m}Pa, ^{234}U and possibly the fairly small amounts of ^{235}U and ^{231}Th. ^{238}U and ^{234}U are alpha emitters, whilst ^{234}Th is a low-energy beta emitter. When a thick sample of a normal uranium compound is brought up to a Geiger tube, the counts recorded are mainly due to the beta particles from ^{234m}Pa which have a fairly high energy. Indeed, if it is necessary to count ^{234}Th, it is usual to count the ^{234m}Pa in equilibrium with it.

Various methods for the separation of ^{234}Th and ^{234m}Pa from commercially available depleted uranium compounds will be discussed in Chapter 7.

It must be emphasised that the remarks which have been made above about the isotopes present in commercially available uranium compounds do not apply to uranium ores. The latter contain appreciable amounts of highly toxic daughter products, such as radium, and for this reason no attempt should be made to extract such daughter products unless first-class facilities are available.

Thorium

From the educational viewpoint the main interest in the uranium series lies in the first three or four members of the family, but the interest in the thorium series is centred on the nuclides which occur near to the middle and near to the end of the decay series.

Radiothorium is isotopic with thorium and will therefore pass into the thorium fraction during any chemical separations such as those involved in the preparation of any thorium compound. After such a separation it will take over 20 years for equilibrium to be fully established owing to the $6\cdot7$ year half-life of mesothorium I. Nevertheless, the presence of the radiothorium in the thorium fraction ensures that appreciable amounts of the decay products will be present provided that a few days is allowed after any separation for the thorium X (half-life $3\cdot64$ days) to grow from the radiothorium. The total activity of a chemically separated specimen of thorium will change somewhat over a period of years as the radiothorium is regenerated from the mesothorium isotopes.

The Emanations

During the early work on the natural radioactive families, it was found that the elements radium and thorium (but not uranium) seemed to have the property of making other materials placed in the same enclosure radioactive. This "induced" activity decayed with a characteristic half-life. The term "emanation" was used to describe the material evolved from radium or thorium which produced this effect. The emanations were found to behave like inert gases and were condensed by liquid air.

It has been shown that this effect is due to the formation of isotopes of the inert gas radon by radium and thorium compounds. Radon follows xenon in the periodic table of the elements. The apparent change in activity of radium and thorium compounds in the presence of a stream of air was also explained by the formation of a radioactive gas.

Radium emanation is the gas known as radon which has a half-life of 3·823 days (Fig. 3.1). It is not emitted by purified uranium compounds, since the long half-lives of ^{234}U and ^{230}Th effectively constitute a break in the decay chain. A similar gas is present in the thorium series. It is known as thoron and is an isotope of radon of half-life 55 sec. The corresponding member of the actinium series is actinon, a further isotope of radon of half-life 3·92 sec.

The gas thoron is very easily obtained from thorium compounds. If ammonium hydroxide is added to a solution of a thorium compound, thorium hydroxide is precipitated. If the precipitate is kept for about a month, the thoron gas will be present in equilibrium with the radiothorium. It will be able to escape from the precipitate and mix with the air in the vessel. If, however, thorium nitrate is used instead of thorium hydroxide, little thoron will leave the material, since it cannot escape from the crystals of the nitrate. The greater the surface area of the material, the greater the proportion of the thoron which escapes. Commercially available thorium hydroxide emits an adequate amount of thoron for most simple experimental work.

The thoron gas evolved from a thorium compound is one of the few short-lived isotopes which can be obtained without any chemical separation. In addition it can be used as a source of further decay products. When thoron decays by alpha emission, thorium A is formed. This has a very short half-life (0·158 sec), emitting an alpha particle. The product atom, thorium B, will recoil with a momentum equal to that of the alpha particle but in the opposite direction. In most cases one or more electrons will be left behind by the recoiling atom. Positively charged ions of thorium B are thus formed which may be collected on a negatively charged plate. The thorium B can be used as a source of further decay products such as thorium C and thorium C″. This method of obtaining decay products has the advantage that no thorium hydroxide is consumed. The decay products are removed on the negatively charged plate when they are required. A clean negatively charged plate will accumulate quite an

c

appreciable amount of activity in the course of a day as the amount of the ^{212}Pb (10·6 hr half-life) builds up according to eqn. (3.3).

Although many useful experiments can be performed using radon and actinon and their decay products, this is virtually out of the question in schools and is not very desirable in other educational establishments since unsealed sources of radium or actinium are required. These alpha emitters are some of the most toxic elements known. The type of experiments which can be performed with the decay products of these elements are very similar to those which are described for thoron and its decay products. For example, a negatively charged plate placed in actinon will acquire an activity due to ^{211}Pb which has a 36·1 min half-life. Sometimes radiothorium is used instead of thorium as a source of thoron gas, since it provides greater activity. For elementary work, however, thorium compounds are perfectly satisfactory and very much less dangerous. Radium, radiothorium and actinium can be formed as highly emanating precipitates by depositing them on ferric hydroxide or barium palmitate.

Other Natural Radioisotopes

A number of naturally occurring radioisotopes are known which do not form part of a decay series. Potassium-40 is of particular interest since potassium is the commonest of the elements which are appreciably radioactive. Naturally occurring potassium compounds contain 0·0119% of ^{40}K which has a half-life of $1·27 \times 10^9$ years. It decays mainly by beta emission of 1·32 MeV maximum energy (89%), the remaining 11% being K capture which results in 1·46 MeV gamma rays being emitted.

The activity of rubidium-87 is easily detected in ordinary rubidium. Although it has a longer half-life than potassium-40, 27·85% of ordinary rubidium is ^{87}Rb. It is a weak beta emitter of energy 0·275 MeV.

Other elements which are naturally active include vanadium, lanthanum, samarium, platinum, lead and some of the rare earths.

CHAPTER 4

Health Physics

HEALTH physics involves the study of the effect of radiation from external and internal sources on biological tissues.

Radiation and Contamination

The dangers associated with the use of radioisotopes can be divided into two main types of hazard, namely radiation and contamination. Further special hazards occur if appreciable quantities of fissile material are kept, but this will not occur in elementary work.

Radioactive substances are often sealed in metal to prevent the escape of any active material. If the sealing is perfect, such a "sealed" or "closed" source is hazardous only because of the radiation it emits. There is no danger of other objects or people being contaminated with the active material. Once the source is put away in a suitable store, there is no further danger.

If an unsealed or "open" source of a radioactive powder, liquid or gas, is being used (or if a leaking sealed source is present), objects can become contaminated with radioactive material. Small amounts of the active material may remain on surfaces even after the bulk of the source has been locked away. Active material from contaminated objects will tend to find its way into people via the mouth, lungs and skin. Eating, smoking or putting anything into the mouth are operations which should be absolutely forbidden in the presence of contamination hazards.

Dose Units

Biological radiation damage is due to chemical reactions initiated by the radiation which result in the formation of toxic chemicals in the body. The damage produced by beta particles, X-rays and gamma rays is proportional to the energy absorbed by unit volume of the body tissues from the radiation. A gamma ray which passes through a person without losing any energy does no harm whatsoever.

The Rad

The rad ("radiation unit") is the unit of absorbed dose. 1 rad is defined as an energy absorption of 100 erg/g or 10^{-5} joule/g.

Relative Biological Effectiveness (R.B.E.)

Some types of radiation such as neutrons, protons and alpha particles produce greater biological damage per unit of energy absorbed in unit volume than beta or X-rays. The relative biological effectiveness of a particular type of radiation of specified particle energy is defined as the ratio

$$\frac{\text{Dose of 200 kV X-rays}}{\text{Dose of the specified type of radiation needed to produce the same effect}}$$

The Rem

The rem is a useful (although not very precise) unit which is used as a measure of the dose received from radiation which does not have a relative biological effectiveness of unity. "Rem" stands for "Röntgen equivalent man" or "Röntgen equivalent mammal".

$$\text{No. of rems} = \text{dose in rads} \times \text{R.B.E.}$$

Thus the rem is the dose of any type of radiation which produces the same effect as 1 rad of 200 kV X-rays.

In the case of X-rays and gamma rays of any energy and most beta particles, the value of the R.B.E. is taken as unity. For beta particles of maximum energy less than 30 keV it may be taken as 1·7. Neutrons have an R.B.E. of 3–10·5 depending on their energy, whereas heavy recoil nuclei have an R.B.E. of 20.

Two other units have often been used in the past and are still found occasionally. They are:

The Röntgen

The Röntgen is the amount of X or gamma radiation which produces ions carrying 1 electrostatic unit of charge of either sign per 0·001293 g of air. The Röntgen should be used only for X and gamma dose rates. This unit corresponds to an absorbed dose of about 84 erg/g in air or about 93 erg/g in water or soft biological tissue. The Röntgen may be taken as equal to the rad for almost all purposes, since health physics measurements do not normally need to be more accurate than ±10%.

The Rep

The rep ("Röntgen equivalent physical") is the amount of any type of radiation which delivers a dose of 93 erg/g to water. The rep may also be taken as approximately equal to the rad.

The definitions of dose units do not convey any practical meaning. Some idea of the dose rates one meets and those which produce effects in exposed persons can be obtained from the following examples and from the recommended maximum permissible doses.

Every person receives a dose of about 100 mrad/year (11 μrad/hr) from cosmic rays and from natural radioisotopes (including those in the body). The dose from the face of a typical luminous watch is 40 mrad/year. A person receives a dose of the order of 1 rad during diagnostic X-ray examination. A dose of 100 rad produces blood changes and some injury including a long-term hazard. There may be nausea and vomiting within 24 hr. A whole body dose of 400–600 rad given at one time will produce death in 50% of human beings in 2–12 weeks. Doses of about 2000 rad are given to limited areas of the body in certain cases of cancer over a period of about a fortnight. Medical instruments, etc., may be sterilised by a dose of about 2,500,000 rad.

Maximum Permissible Doses

The maximum permissible dose a person may receive varies with the type of work he is doing. From genetic considerations the International Commission on Radiological Protection have recommended that the average dose received by a whole population should not exceed 2 rem up to the age of 30 years (excluding doses received in medical examinations). In view of the greater danger to young people, the Ministry of Education have recommended[7] that no pupil should receive a dose of more than 50 mrad of external radiation in any one year as a result of experimental work in schools. This same limit should be applied to students working in establishments of further education unless the establishment concerned has obtained approval to carry out radioisotope work at a higher level than that normally carried out in schools.

In educational establishments other than those working at school level, the maximum permissible body dose is that for industrial workers, namely 1·5 rem per year. Nevertheless, in the case of medically supervised "designated" persons the total dose received may be as large as $5(N-18)$ rems where N is the age of the person in years. This amount is subject to a limit of 3 rem in any calendar quarter. Certain parts of the body may receive a somewhat higher dose, e.g. 75 rem/year to the hands, forearms, feet and ankles of designated persons.

It must be emphasised that these doses are maximum permissible ones; every effort should be made to keep the dose as low as possible, especially where young people are concerned.

Dose Rate Calculations

The maximum doses permitted in schools are so low that it is difficult to measure them with normal ionisation chamber monitors. The doses may, however, be estimated by calculation.

1. *Alpha Radiation*

The alpha radiation emitted by radioisotopes will not penetrate the skin and therefore it presents a negligible radiation hazard provided that sealed sources are used.

2. *Beta Radiation*

Accurate beta dose rate calculations are not easy to make, but an approximate formula for the dose from a point source is

$$D = \frac{300CT}{d^2},$$

where D = dose rate in rads per hour, C = source strength in curies, T = the attenuation of the rays as they pass through the air, d = distance from the source in feet.

The factor T is equal to $2^{-x/d_{\frac{1}{2}}}$ where x is the amount of air in milligrammes per square centimetre between the source and the point at which the measurement is being made (1 ft of air = 40 mg/cm²) and $d_{\frac{1}{2}}$ is the half-thickness of the beta particles in milligrammes per square centimetre. If E is the maximum energy of the radiation in megaelectron volts, $d_{\frac{1}{2}}$ is approximately equal to $46E^{3/2}$. Thus the factor T is not especially easy to calculate, but for elementary work it is suggested that T is put equal to unity so that an overestimated dose rate is obtained which provides a factor of safety.

As an example, let us calculate the dose rate at 3 in. from a 100 μcurie source of a beta emitter assuming $T = 1$.

$$C = 10^{-4} \text{ curie}$$
$$d = \tfrac{1}{4} \text{ ft}$$
$$D = 300C/d^2 = \frac{300 \times 10^{-4}}{(\tfrac{1}{4})^2} = 0\cdot48 \text{ rad/hr} = 480 \text{ mrad/hr}.$$

This dose rate constitutes quite an appreciable hazard. One of the main dangers from beta radiation is to the cornea of the eye. One should never look closely at an unshielded beta source of more than about a microcurie. A piece of fairly thick glass may be used as a shield to prevent the radiation from reaching the eye.

3. *Gamma Dose Rate Calculations*

Gamma radiation is not absorbed by shielding nearly so easily as beta radiation and therefore gamma dose rate calculations are of great importance. Air absorption is small unless the source distance is large; it is neglected in the following calculations which are strictly applicable only to point sources.

Method A. The dose rate in rads per hour D, at a distance of d ft from a point source of gamma radiation, is given by the approximate formula

$$D = 6CE/d^2,$$

where C = the source strength in curies and E = the total energy of the radiation per disintegration in megaelectron volts.

This formula may be used to calculate the gamma dose rate at 3 in. from a 100 μcurie source of the beta–gamma emitter caesium-137:

$$C = 10^{-4} \text{ curie}$$
$$E = 0 \cdot 662 \text{ MeV (from tables of isotope data}^{(8, 9)})$$
$$d = \tfrac{1}{4} \text{ ft.}$$

Hence $D = \dfrac{6 \times 10^{-4} \times 0 \cdot 662}{(\tfrac{1}{4})^2} = 6 \cdot 4 \times 10^{-3} \text{ rad/hr}$
$$= 6 \cdot 4 \text{ mrad/hr.}$$

Actually the gamma radiation arises from the nuclide ^{137m}Ba which is continually being formed from ^{137}Cs. However, only

92% of the ^{137}Cs atoms form ^{137m}Ba and therefore the dose rate which has been calculated should be multiplied by 0·92. This gives a gamma dose rate of about 5·9 mrad/hr. In addition there is the previously calculated beta dose rate of 480 mrad/hr which must be added to the gamma dose rate to ascertain the total dose rate.

As a further example, the dose rate at 2 ft from a typical industrial radiography source of 1 curie of cobalt-60 will be found. This isotope emits two gamma rays of 1·17 and 1·33 MeV per disintegration. Thus the total gamma energy is 2·5 MeV.

$$D = 6CE/d^2 = (6 \times 1 \times 2·5)/4 = 3·75 \text{ rad/hr.}$$

A 10 μcurie source of cobalt-60 (which is a typical strength for student use) would, of course, give 10^{-5} of this dose rate, namely 0·0375 mrad/hr at the same distance of 2 ft.

Method B. Some isotopes such as ^{131}I emit many gamma rays of different energies, but not every disintegration results in a gamma ray of each energy being emitted. In such cases the calculation of the average gamma ray energy per disintegration (which is required for use in the formula $D = 6CE/d^2$) can be tedious and the following method is to be preferred.

A table of specific gamma ray emissions for the various elements is required.[9,10] This gives the dose rate in rads per hour at 1 cm from 1 mcurie of each of the common gamma-emitting isotopes. The specific gamma-ray emission was formerly known as the k factor. Some values are given in Appendix 2.

Let us repeat the calculation of the dose rate at 3 in. (7·6 cm) from a 100 μcurie source of ^{137}Cs. The specific gamma-ray emission for ^{137}Cs is 3·1 rad/hr/mcurie at 1 cm. For a 100 μcurie source at 1 cm the dose rate will therefore be 0·31 rad/hr. At 7·6 cm it will be $0·31/(7·6)^2$ rad/hr = 5·36 mrad/hr. This is in good agreement with the value found previously, since the equation $6CE/d^2$ gives values of dose rates which are intentionally a little high.

Method C. The methods described previously are very useful for practical gamma dose rate calculations. The method now to be described is more directly related to theory, but (like the first method) is not very suitable for use with isotopes which have a complicated decay scheme.

It is necessary to know the linear energy transfer (L.E.T.) for the radiation concerned in body tissue. The L.E.T. is the mean energy given up per photon in passing through 1 cm of tissue. If the L.E.T. is multiplied by the number of photons per square centimetre per second, one obtains the number of megaelectron volts absorbed per cubic centimetre per second. 1 MeV = $1 \cdot 6 \times 10^{-6}$ erg and 1 rad is a dose of 100 erg/g. Therefore a dose of 1 MeV/g is $1 \cdot 6 \times 10^{-8}$ rad.

If L is the linear energy transfer and N the photon flux, the dose rate is $1 \cdot 6 \times 10^{-8} LN$ rad/sec or $5 \cdot 76 \times 10^{-5} LN$ rad/hr.

In the case of a 1 curie source of cobalt-60 at a distance of 2 m, the value of L is $0 \cdot 038$ MeV/cm for the $1 \cdot 33$ MeV gamma rays and $0 \cdot 036$ MeV/cm for the $1 \cdot 17$ MeV photons. One photon of each of these energies is emitted per disintegration, the gamma flux due to each photon energy at a distance of 2 m being

$$\frac{\text{No. of disintegrations per second}}{\text{Surface area of sphere of radius 2 m}} = \frac{3 \cdot 7 \times 10^{10}}{4 \pi (200)^2}$$

$$= 7 \cdot 36 \times 10^4 \text{ photons/cm}^2 \text{ sec.}$$

Total dose rate = $5 \cdot 76 \times 10^{-5} \times 7 \cdot 36 \times 10^4 (0 \cdot 038 + 0 \cdot 036)$
= $0 \cdot 314$ rad/hr.

The value of L for a gamma ray energy of E MeV may be estimated in the following way. The fraction F of the incident photons absorbed in 1 cm of the body tissue is given by the approximate equations[11]

$$F = 0 \cdot 0258 (1 + E) \text{ for } 0 \cdot 07 \text{ MeV} < E < 0 \cdot 5 \text{ MeV}$$
$$\text{and} \quad F = 0 \cdot 0369 (1 - 0 \cdot 08 E) \text{ for } 0 \cdot 5 \text{ MeV} < E < 6 \text{ MeV,}$$

and the value of L is found from the equation $L = EF$ MeV/cm.

Beta and Gamma Dose Rates

The beta and gamma dose rates at 3 in. from a 100 μcurie source of ^{137}Cs have already been found to be 480 and 5·4 mrad/hr respectively. In general it is to be expected that the beta dose rate at a certain distance from a source of specified activity will be many times the gamma dose rate at the same distance from a gamma source of the same activity, since beta radiation is much more strongly absorbed than gamma radiation. Nevertheless, this does not necessarily mean that the beta hazard is very much greater than that due to the gamma radiation. The beta rays will be able to penetrate only a few centimetres beneath the skin, whereas the gamma rays may affect the whole body.

For beta particles of about 2 MeV, 10 beta particles/cm² sec correspond to a dose of about 1 mrad/hr, whilst 1 mrad is about $3·6 \times 10^4$ beta particles/cm². The dose rate for beta particles of about 0·4 MeV is about half of these values.

In the case of gamma radiation of photon energy E,

$$1 \text{ mrad} = \frac{1·9 \times 10^6}{E} \text{ photons/cm}^2$$

and

$$1 \text{ mrad/hr} = \frac{530}{E} \text{ photons/cm}^2/\text{sec.}$$

Beta Shielding

Beta shielding presents few problems, since a thickness of 3 g/cm² of any material will absorb beta particles up to an energy of 4 MeV, whilst beta particles of 0·5 MeV are completely absorbed by a thickness of 0·2 g/cm². Generally a sheet of a transparent material such as glass or perspex is most convenient. The use of a light material also minimises bremsstrahlung production.

Gamma Shielding

Gamma rays are not completely absorbed by matter, but have their intensity reduced by a factor which depends on the atomic number of the absorber and the gamma-ray energy. Some typical examples are shown in Table 4.1, but more detailed information is available.[12]

TABLE 4.1

Lead (MeV)	Thickness (in.)	Fraction transmitted	Concrete (MeV)	Thickness (in.)	Fraction transmitted
1	0·35	0·5	1	4	0·5
1	1·5	0·1	1	12	0·1
1	2·75	0·01	1	23	0·01
3	0·6	0·5	Iron		
3	2·5	0·1	1	0·6	0·5
			1	3·3	0·1
			1	6·0	0·01

Gamma shielding should always be placed as close as possible to the source, since this reduces the weight of shielding required by a very large factor.

Precautions in the Use of Closed Sources

Sealed sources should not be handled. It can be seen from the inverse square law that the dose rate at about 1 mm from a true point source is 10,000 times that at 10 cm. Thus forceps of about 1 ft in length are convenient for the handling of small sealed sources. Sources should be kept in a container which is suitably marked and which provides adequate shielding. When working with sealed sources it should be remembered that the dose is dependent on the three factors of time, distance and shielding employed.

Measurement of Gamma Dose Rate

A sensitive ionisation chamber portable dose rate meter does not usually have a sensitivity of less than about 0·2 mrad/hr. The small dose rates used in elementary work will often be undetectable. Some commercial dose rate meters employing Geiger tubes are available and can be made much more sensitive, although they may not be so accurate as the ionisation chamber instruments. For a given photon flux the dose rate increases approximately in proportion to the photon energy, but the efficiency of a Geiger tube also increases in proportion to the photon energy if the latter exceeds about $0 \cdot 3$ MeV. Thus a Geiger tube has a response which is approximately proportional to the dose rate.

Contamination

Contamination hazards are rather more difficult to assess than purely radiation hazards and in work at school level they present a much greater danger. Contamination hazards are controlled by taking suitable precautions during experimental work, by limiting the amount of radioactive material which can be used in any one type of laboratory and by periodic monitoring of surfaces and possibly of personnel. The precautions required depend on the amount and on the toxicity of the nuclides used.

Radionuclides are classified into four groups according to their toxicity.[13] Class 1 isotopes are of very high radiotoxicity; they consist of alpha emitters and strontium-90. The use of unsealed class 1 isotopes in schools is prohibited. Class 2 isotopes are highly toxic, but include some very useful ones such as ^{131}I and [144]Ce. The large class 3 group of moderately toxic isotopes includes ^{32}P, ^{35}S, [65]Zn, etc. Tritium is included in the low toxicity class 4.

If normal chemical operations are being carried out in a good class laboratory reserved for radioisotope work (a "grade C" laboratory), the maximum recommended amounts are 100 μcurie of a class 2 nuclide, 1 mcurie of a class 3 nuclide or 10 mcurie of a class 4 nuclide. These quantities should be reduced by a factor of 100 if dry and dusty operations are involved, but may be increased a by factor of 100 when the isotopes are kept as stock solutions.

Precautions in the Use of Unsealed Isotopes

Naturally occurring radioactive elements present no greater hazard than many other poisonous chemicals which are commonly used. Indeed, zinc uranyl acetate is a common chemical reagent. The maximum permissible amounts of natural uranium and thorium which may be ingested per day by an occupationally exposed worker are, according to the recommendations of the International Commission on Radiological Protection, 0.7 and 0.04 μcurie respectively. This means that 2 g of elemental uranium or 0.35 g of elemental thorium would have to be ingested per day in order to reach the maximum permissible dose. (This neglects any effects of the chemical toxicity of these materials.) Such an amount could not be ingested accidentally if suitable precautions are taken, and the hazard due to these elements is therefore very small. Like all heavy metals, uranium and thorium are potent chemical poisons, and care must be taken to avoid ingestion. The specific activity of other naturally occurring materials such as potassium, rubidium, carbon, etc., is very low indeed and they offer virtually no radiation hazard.

Invisible amounts of artificially produced nuclides can be extremely hazardous. The weights of 1 mcurie of some materials is shown in Table 1.1 (p. 10). Such an amount could easily be picked up as an invisible deposit on the end of a person's finger and would present a considerable hazard. Although the precautions to be adopted when using unsealed isotopes vary considerably with the amounts of the material and its toxicity, the following safety measures should be regarded as essential when unsealed artificially produced isotopes are being used.

A laboratory coat must be worn.

Rubber gloves must be worn during the preparation of a sample, but should be removed before counting is commenced.

All work other than counting must be carried out over a large unbreakable tray lined with absorbent paper.

Liquids should be transferred with suitable safety pipettes, no mouth operations whatsoever being permissible even with non-radioactive liquids.

When possible a vessel containing a radioactive solution should be placed inside a larger vessel so that the liquid will be retained if the inner vessel is overturned.

The bench surface should be covered with a detachable non-absorbent cover.

Work with unsealed isotopes should not be undertaken by anyone having an open wound on the hand or forearm.

All contaminated glassware must be cleaned in a sink reserved for that purpose. The sink and apparatus should be monitored afterwards.

Students must never be allowed to dispose of radioactive waste. This should be done by a member of staff who enters a record of the disposal showing the isotope, the amount, the method of disposal and the date.

Monitoring

Bench surfaces, etc., should be periodically monitored if unsealed artificially produced nuclides are used. A long glass-walled Geiger tube (e.g. type B12) may be used with, for example, the A.E.R.E. 1021B equipment, but this will not detect low-energy beta particles from ^{14}C or ^{35}S. Scintillation probes are available which will detect alpha, beta and gamma contamination; the window is very thin.

The maximum amount of contamination of clothing and parts of the body which can be permitted is about 10^{-4} μcurie/cm^2. This corresponds to about 5 counts/sec when the beta probe of the 1021B equipment is held close to the surface.[14] An MX123 or EHM2 mica end-window tube will give about $1 \cdot 5$ counts/sec when near a surface contaminated to the same level.[14] The maximum permissible amount of bench contamination is about 10 times that for clothing and parts of the body. In the unlikely event of any alpha contamination being present, it should not exceed one-tenth of the maximum permissible level for beta contamination.

These levels of contamination apply to technical colleges. In schools the level of contamination should be reduced until it cannot be detected with a suitable Geiger tube.

Maximum Permissible Levels

Maximum levels have been recommended for the amounts of various radioisotopes which may be present in the body of an occupationally exposed worker.[15, 9] In assessing these levels consideration is given to the places in the body where each isotope concentrates, the effective half-life in the body, etc. The effective half-life t is related to the half-life $t_{\frac{1}{2}}$ of the isotope and to the biological half-life t_b of the element.

$$t = \frac{t_b t_{\frac{1}{2}}}{(t_b + t_{\frac{1}{2}})}.$$

t_b is the time taken for half of the element to be eliminated from the body. The hazard due to some isotopes, such as ^{131}I, is very much increased by the fact that a large proportion of the amount of this material present in the body concentrates in the thyroid. The thyroid is a relatively small organ and the maximum permissible body burden for ^{131}I is determined by thyroid damage. Thus the thyroid is the critical organ for this isotope.

Recommended maximum permissible levels for various isotopes present in drinking water and in inhaled air have been published.[15, 9, 16] They apply to persons continuously exposed in the course of their work; in other cases they should be reduced by a factor of 10. These maximum permissible concentrations are based on the intake of the isotope by a standard man who will accumulate the maximum permissible body burden as a result of a 50-year occupational exposure to air and water contaminated at these levels. The maximum permissible concentrations may not be the same for soluble and insoluble materials.

Film Badge Service

The Radiological Protection Service (of the Ministry of Health and the Medical Research Council) of Clifton Avenue, Belmont, Sutton, Surrey, provide a film badge service. Films may be obtained regularly from this organisation and, after being worn in a special badge for about a month, are returned to the Radiological Protection Service for development and dose assessment. Doses of 20 mrad up to 2000 rad can be measured in this way by the use of a film coated with a sensitive emulsion on one side and a much less sensitive one on the other side. The filters employed in a badge enable some assessment of the type of radiation to be made as well as the total dose received.

It is difficult to give definite advice as to when the use of film badges is desirable. The writer feels that film badges should be worn by those people using sources of an activity greater than about 50 μcurie regularly or greater than about 300 μcurie occasionally. However, the type of radiation and, in the case of unsealed nuclides, the radiotoxicity of the isotopes concerned, should be taken into account. All persons using X-ray equipment should wear a film badge, since the dose rates can be very high.

If a film badge indicates that a person has received a dose in any one month which is appreciably greater than one-twelfth of the maximum permissible annual dose for that person, an investigation should be made into the reason why the dose was incurred and steps should be taken to prevent a repetition. In elementary work very high doses are not likely to occur.

CHAPTER 5

Some Practical Considerations

Sources

Most elementary work in physics involves a study of the properties of the various types of radiation. Sealed sources can therefore be employed. In chemical and biological work, however, unsealed sources are normally required. A considerable number of radiochemical experiments can be carried out with naturally occurring radionuclides; this almost eliminates the contamination hazard and provides a useful introduction to subsequent work with artificially produced nuclides. Establishments using unsealed artificially produced nuclides must take a considerable amount of trouble to ensure that the contamination hazard is kept small. A laboratory which is kept solely for radioisotope work is un-doubtedly desirable.

Sealed sources of artificially produced nuclides are especially useful for experiments where a pure alpha, beta or gamma source is required. Uranium and thorium compounds emit a mixture of alpha, beta and gamma radiation of various energies and it is not possible to obtain the alpha or beta radiation alone. Sealed sources of a half-life greater than a few years are most economical for educational use.

Small sealed alpha sources containing about $0 \cdot 1$ μcurie of americium-241 or plutonium-239 are very useful. The low energy gamma photons emitted by these isotopes do not produce a very noticeable count rate when a Geiger tube is used. A strontium-90 source of about $0 \cdot 1$ μcurie may be obtained as a sealed source of energetic beta radiation. Similar sources of thallium-204 and carbon-14 may be used if beta radiation of moderate and of low energy respectively is required. Owing to the low efficiency of a Geiger tube for gamma-ray detection, a somewhat larger gamma source is desirable. A source of 10 μcurie of cobalt-60 is suitable. Caesium-137 may be used if gamma radiation of a lower energy is required.

Although neutron sources are undoubtedly quite useful, even at school level, for preparing small amounts of short-lived radio-active materials, their purchase cannot really be justified except in courses of degree standard. Apart from the cost of such sources, the full provisions of the *Code of Practice*[13] apply to establishments which use them and this will entail a considerable amount of administrative work. There are very few neutron sources in British schools, although they may be found in many of the larger colleges.

Purchasing Unsealed Isotopes

Until recently British educational establishments (other than those working under the full provisions of the *Code of Practice*[13]) were permitted to purchase unsealed artificially produced radio-isotopes only from the Radiochemical Centre, Amersham, Buckinghamshire. A catalogue of sealed and unsealed sources is available. Small quantities of alpha and beta emitters are sent by registered post in sealed cans. Small amounts of gamma emitters are packed in lead, sealed in a can and sent by registered post, but somewhat larger amounts of gamma emitters (exceeding about a millicurie) are sent by through train and must be collected by the addressee since the railway will not deliver them.

Unsealed sources are normally dispensed in aqueous solution, the volume being about 1–10 ml. Radioisotopes can also be ordered in solid form. If a material has a short half-life, the amount of material dispatched is usually slightly above that ordered so that it will decay to the required amount at a specified time.

Most radioisotope prices are quoted for 1 mcurie as a minimum in the Radiochemical Centre's catalogue. Although establishments which are working at school level may not require a millicurie of any one isotope, they will nevertheless be charged for this amount. The isotopes which are priced for smaller quantities are generally the expensive cyclotron produced ones.

Considerable thought should be given to the choice of isotope. Although the long-term contamination hazard may, in the case of some experiments, be reduced by the use of a fairly short-lived isotope (such as ^{131}I or ^{32}P), the frequent use of such materials involves repeated expenditure. The total cost of such materials over a period may exceed the amount which could reasonably be allocated for radioisotope purchase by a school.

As far as possible nuclides of low toxicity should be used. Very few schools will be able to allocate a small laboratory solely for radiochemical work, and great attention must therefore be paid to contamination hazards. Although pupils under 16 years of age are not permitted to be in laboratories when radio-isotope experiments are being carried out by other pupils,[17] they may meet a contamination hazard if they use labora-tories in which unsealed substances have been used by other classes.

Arrangements have recently been made for very small amounts of unsealed radioisotopes in the form of tablets to be placed on the market for educational use. Each tablet contains about $0 \cdot 1$ μcurie of the isotope absorbed on a pellet of a chemically similar inactive material. It is expected that isotopes such as ^{45}Ca, ^{110m}Ag, ^{35}S, ^{14}C, ^{22}Na and a ^{55}Fe/^{59}Fe mixture will be available from stock, whilst the shorter-lived ^{131}I and ^{32}P will be avail-able when the demand warrants it.[18] The purchase of very small quantities of radioisotopes in this way is more economical than a purchase of the same amount from the Radiochemical Centre, but the reverse applies if more than a few microcuries of any one isotope is required. The main advantage obtained from the purchase of unsealed isotopes in tablet form is the elimination of most of the contamination dangers associated with nuclides of relatively high specific activity; the tablets are therefore very suitable for use in schools and in the smaller colleges.

Geiger Counting Equipment

Commercial Geiger counting equipment may be divided into two main types, namely economical equipment intended for use in schools and professional counting equipment.

The economical school type of equipment usually consists of an end-window counter with a plug-in base which is inter-changeable with a 5 ml liquid sample counter; the Geiger tube is connected to an economical scaler or ratemeter which contains an H.T. supply for the tube. The price of a ratemeter or scaler of this type is usually a little over £50 and that of the Geiger tubes just under £10 each. When this type of equipment is used, no correction for lost counts due to the finite resolving time is normally made. This simplifies the handling of the results in elementary work.

In the economical school type of equipment a lead castle is not usually used, although it is possible to make one. The Geiger tube base is usually mounted in a small box which is connected to the scaler or ratemeter by a piece of co-axial cable. For counting solid samples some form of support must be made for the Geiger tube. This will allow the tube to be inverted so that the end win-dow is about 1 cm above the sample which is placed in one of the small aluminium counting trays or planchets. The position of the tube relative to the sample must be reproducible. A shelf should be placed between the sample and the end window of the Geiger tube to support the absorbers.

The internal power supply for the Geiger tube in most types of economical counting equipment covers a range of about 250–550 V and may not be suitable for use with halogen quenched tubes which require a somewhat higher voltage than the types intended for school use (e.g. the MX123).

Almost all radiochemical work at school level, including the experiments to be described, can be carried out with the simple equipment intended for school use. It is not to be expected, how-ever, that the accuracy obtained with such equipment will be so good as that obtained with professional equipment.

Professional Geiger counting equipment normally uses an end-window tube which is mounted in a lead castle or a liquid sample tube of 10 ml capacity placed in another type of lead castle. The pulses from the Geiger tube pass into a quenching probe unit which provides an accurately known resolving time, often 400 μsec. A professional scaler may provide more facilities than the economical types intended for school use. For example, the power supply for the Geiger tube will usually be variable over a range of about 250–2000 V so that organic or halogen quenched tubes can be used. It may be able to count at a higher speed than the economical school equipment and may incorporate an automatic timer which will stop the counting after a preset time or after a preset number of counts have been recorded.

Professional ratemeters and scalers are priced at about £100 upwards, depending on the facilities provided. Quenching probe units (which determine the resolving time) are obtainable for about £25, whilst the cost of lead castles varies from about £20 to £60, depending on the amount of shielding, etc., which is employed.

It is important to note that if the resolving time correction is omitted when a quenching probe unit is being used, the resulting errors may exceed those when the economical school type of equipment is being used. The quenching probe unit increases the resolving time and therefore the losses, but it gives the resolving time a definite value which enables corrections to be made for the losses.

It is felt that scalers are generally much more useful than ratemeters for individual student experiments owing to their greater accuracy. Ratemeters are nevertheless very useful when it is desirable for an approximate reading of the counting rate to be continuously or quickly available. Ratemeters are particularly useful in monitoring instruments and for lecture demonstrations; for these purposes they should be fitted with a loudspeaker which will give an audible indication of the counting rate.

Teachers and lecturers who are willing to construct their own scalers and ratemeters can do so at a fraction of the cost of new equipment. Various suitable circuits have been published.[19-23] From time to time the United Kingdom Atomic Energy Authority has made items of older types of counting equipment, etc., available to educational institutions at a very small fraction of their normal cost. This is an ideal source of supply for those who have a good practical knowledge of nucleonic circuitry and who are willing to spend some time putting equipment into good working order; it is not recommended, however, that those who have no particular interest in counting equipment should use this source of supply.

A full set of about forty aluminium and lead absorbers will cost about £10–£20. It is often possible to make some of these from sheet aluminium and lead, but it is doubtful if a very high accuracy will be achieved. Thin aluminium foil absorbers should be supported in a plastic frame.

Types of Detector

The halogen quenched Geiger tubes shown in Table 5.1 are felt to be some of the most suitable tubes for educational use which are manufactured in the United Kingdom. Those in the upper part of the table with plug-in bases are most suitable for use in economical school equipment, whilst those in the lower part are more suitable for use in professional type equipment in lead castles. The plug-in gamma tubes have metal walls and are unsuitable for the detection of any other type of radiation. The plug-in end-window tubes are supplied with a plastic or metal guard which helps to prevent damage by students, but which also reduces the effective window area by an appreciable factor and thus reduces beta counting rates. No such guards are used with end-window tubes intended for mounting in lead castles, since the lead castle offers a considerable amount of protection to the very delicate end window.

Pulse electroscopes have their uses in school work where the aim is rather more academic than practical. If pupils have already used such electroscopes in their electrical work, the use of such

TABLE 5.1. TABLE OF HALOGEN QUENCHED TUBES SUITABLE FOR EDUCATIONAL USE

	Typical operating voltage	Window thickness (mg/cm²)	Window diameter (mm)	Typical background (c/min)*	Liquid sample volume (ml)	Base	Manufacturer
Tubes for use without lead castles: End-window tubes:							
MX168 } MX108 }	425	3·5–4·0	18	45	—	B2A	Mullard Ltd.
ST1	550	—	18	45	—	6 ft. co-axial lead with P.E.T. socket	20th Century Electronics Ltd.
ST2	450	3	18	45	—	B2A	20th Century Electronics Ltd.
Liquid sample tubes:							
MX142	425	15	—	10	5	B2A	Mullard Ltd.
M6Ha	375	23–35	—	40	10	B2A	20th Century Electronics Ltd.
M2H } CV2886 }	425	20	—	10	5	B2A	20th Century Electronics Ltd.

Gamma tubes:							
MX115 ⎫ MX180 ⎬	425	(375)	—	45	—	B2A	Mullard Ltd.
G5H	375	—	—	45	—	B2A	20th Century Electronics Ltd.
5GH	375	—	—	45	—	B2A	M.O. Valve Co. Ltd.
12GH	375	—	—	90	—	B2A	M.O. Valve Co. Ltd.
Tubes for use in lead castles: End window:							
MX123	650	1·5–2·5	25	10	—	Soldering lug	Mullard Ltd.
TX123	650	1·5–2·5	25	10	—	Soldering lug	20th Century Electronics Ltd.
EW3H	600	1·5–2·5	25	10	—	International Octal	20th Century Electronics Ltd.
Liquid sample:							
MX124 ⎫ MX124/01 ⎬	400	30	—	12	10	Mercury pool connection	Mullard Ltd.
M6H	425	30	—	12	10	Mercury pool connection	Mullard Ltd.

* The background counting rates quoted are those for typical unshielded tubes, except in the case of tubes intended fo use in lead castles, when they are typical values for shielded tubes.

instruments will make the ionising power of radiation rather more easily apparent than the use of Geiger tubes.

Scintillation detectors are very useful for some types of more advanced work, but it is somewhat doubtful whether they have a place in experimental work at school level. They are especially useful when a high efficiency gamma detector or an alpha detector of a fairly large sensitive area is needed. The cost of a simple scintillation counting system will usually be between £100 and £200, but a modern gamma-ray spectrometer (including the equipment for pulse amplitude analysis) will be much more expensive.

Many semiconductor detectors for professional work are priced at about £50, but during the past few years some economical detectors of this type have appeared on the educational market priced at about £10. The sensitive area of these economical detectors is quite small. The detectors must be connected to a preamplifier which is in turn connected to a scaler of the same type as those used for Geiger counting. Simple preamplifiers for economical semiconductor detectors are available commercially at prices of the order of £20 each, but simple circuits using four OC44 transistors for alpha counting and seven OC44 transistors in an amplifier of higher gain for alpha, beta or gamma counting have been published[24]; such circuits are very suitable for the amateur constructor or a school science club.

In general it is felt that schools and small colleges commencing radioisotope work at an elementary level should be recommended to obtain Geiger counting equipment at first, especially if the funds available are very limited. Semiconductor detectors and suitable preamplifiers can easily be purchased at a subsequent date and used with the scalers which have been obtained for Geiger counting. Semiconductor detectors are much more suitable for alpha detection than for beta or gamma work at an elementary level; they are therefore likely to be of much more use to a physicist than to a chemist, since the use of unsealed alpha sources (other than uranium or thorium) should be avoided for reasons of safety. Foils are available which can be placed in front of a semiconductor detector for neutron counting, but these are not likely to be of use in elementary work.

Photographic Techniques

The photographic method of detection has the advantage that it provides a student with a permanent record of an experiment. X-ray film is not especially cheap, but it is appreciably more sensitive to ionising radiation than a normal fast photographic emulsion. This is an important advantage when weak sources are being used. Generally envelope-wrapped X-ray film is well worth the extra cost, since it is so much more convenient to handle before development. X-ray film also has the advantage that it can be processed in a dark room illuminated by a normal X-ray safelight (green), whereas all really high-speed emulsions intended for normal photography are panchromatic and must be handled in complete darkness. X-ray film can be developed in an ordinary developer, but it is preferable to use an X-ray developer for optimum results.

Nuclear emulsions provide a good way of investigating alpha particle tracks. The emulsion contains a greater proportion of silver bromide than an ordinary photographic emulsion, but the grain is much finer; the tracks of alpha particles may be seen as fine lines under a high-power microscope. Nuclear emulsions are usually thicker than normal photographic emulsions, but emulsion thicknesses exceeding about 100 μ should be avoided, if possible, since the processing of such emulsions becomes more difficult with increasing thickness. Nuclear emulsions can be handled in a yellowish-brown safelight, but the image cannot, of course, be examined until the processing has been completed.

Half-life Experiments

In order to follow the decay of a radioisotope during a reasonably short time, a radionuclide with a half-life of not more than a few minutes must be used. Such materials cannot be purchased, since they would decay during transport. They can be made with reactors or cyclotrons and small amounts can be made with neutron sources. Undoubtedly the most convenient method of obtaining short-lived nuclides for school use involves their separation from a long-lived parent isotope with which they are in secular equilibrium. The short-lived daughter products in the uranium and thorium series are very convenient for this purpose. Details of the separation of various short-lived nuclides will be discussed in Chapter 7.

Daughter products may also be separated from certain artificially produced nuclides. For example, ^{144}Pr (17 min half-life) remains in solution when its parent, ^{144}Ce, is precipitated as ceric iodate[25], whilst ^{137m}Ba (2·6 min) may be precipitated as barium sulphate from a solution containing ^{137}Cs. For short demonstration experiments the shorter-lived ^{106}Rh (30 sec) may be conveniently obtained from ^{106}Ru. Nevertheless, the use of naturally occurring daughter products is to be preferred owing to the much lower contamination hazard.

Half-life determination together with absorption experiments may be used for the identification of isotopes.

Half-life Graphs

In order to obtain a linear decay curve, a graph of $\log_{10}$ (corrected count rate) may be plotted against time (Fig. 5.1).

$$N = N_0 \, e^{-\lambda t} \quad \text{[eqn. (1.3)].}$$

Differentiating,
$$-\frac{dN}{dt} = \lambda N_0 \, e^{-\lambda t},$$

Hence
$$\log_e \left(-\frac{dN}{dt} \right) = \log_e (\lambda N_0) - \lambda t.$$

If the efficiency of the detector is E, the counting rate

$$n = E \left(-\frac{dN}{dt} \right).$$

Thus
$$\log_e \left(\frac{n}{E} \right) = \log_e (\lambda N_0) - \lambda t.$$

Changing the base of the logarithms to 10,

$$\log_{10} n - \log_{10} E = \log_{10} (\lambda N_0) - \left(\frac{\lambda}{2 \cdot 303}\right) t.$$

E and λN_0 are constants. Therefore the gradient of a graph of $\log_{10} n$ against t will be equal to $-\lambda/2 \cdot 303$. Using eqn. (1.4),

$$t_{\frac{1}{2}} = \frac{0 \cdot 6931}{\lambda} = \frac{-0 \cdot 6931}{2 \cdot 303 \times \text{gradient}} = \frac{-0 \cdot 3008}{\text{gradient}} \tag{5.1}$$

A rather easier way of obtaining the half-life, especially for non-mathematical students, involves plotting the corrected count rate against time on semilogarithmic graph paper (i.e. graph paper graduated logarithmically along the count-rate axis and linearly along the time axis). The graph, in the case of a single isotope decaying to a stable daughter, should be a straight-line one. The count rate at zero time is read from the graph and the time t at which the count rate is less than this initial rate by a factor of 8 is found. The half-life is then equal to one-third of t. Sometimes it may be more convenient to find the time for the isotope to decay to one-quarter or one-sixteenth of its initial activity, in which case the half-life is one-half or one-quarter of this time respectively.

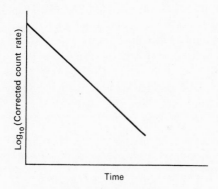

FIG. 5.1. A decay graph.

Half-life from a Growth Curve

In some cases it will be found that a long-lived parent isotope A which emits alpha or weak beta particles decays into another short-lived isotope B which emits more penetrating beta particles. The decay product of B is stable or emits particles of low penetrating power or has a much longer half-life than B. If the isotope A is chemically separated from B, the amount of B present in the sample will grow from zero until its rate of disintegration is equal to that of A. Counting may be carried out using an absorber which will remove all the radiation from A so that the counting rate increases from almost zero as the amount of B present in the sample increases. The problem arises as to how the half-life of B can be determined from the increasing count rate.

The growth of the nuclide B is represented by eqn. (3.3):

$$N_B = K(1 - e^{-\lambda_B t}),$$

where $N_B =$ the number of atoms of B present in the sample, $K =$ a constant, $\lambda_B =$ the radioactive constant of B, $t =$ the time after B was separated from A.

Neither a linear nor a logarithmic plot of the counting rate against time will produce a linear graph. If the final counting rate n_0 can be found when B has reached its equilibrium activity, each observed value of the counting rate may be subtracted from n_0. The resulting values are the counting rates which would have been obtained from the separated fraction of B (containing no A) at the same counting efficiency. They may be plotted in the normal way and the half-life deduced from eqn. (5.1).

If the asymptotic final value of the counting rate is unknown, the results may be treated according to the following method. On differentiating eqn. (3.3), one obtains

$$\frac{dN_B}{dt} = K\lambda_B\, e^{-\lambda_B t}$$

or, as the counting rate n is proportional to the number of atoms of B present in the sample, and λ_B is constant,

$$\frac{dn}{dt} = C\, e^{-\lambda_B t}, \quad \text{where } C \text{ is another constant.}$$

Hence
$$\log_e \left(\frac{dn}{dt} \right) = \log_e C - \lambda_B t$$

$$\log_{10} \left(\frac{dn}{dt} \right) = \log_{10} C - \frac{\lambda_B}{2 \cdot 303} t. \tag{5.2}$$

Hence a graph of $\log_{10} (dn/dt)$ against time is a straight line of gradient

$$\frac{-\lambda_B}{2 \cdot 303}.$$

Values of dn/dt may be found for various times from a graph of n against time. λ_B is found from the slope of a graph of $\log_{10}(dn/dt)$ against time, and the half-life is deduced.

The following alternative method can be used to find the asymptotic final counting rate if the time of separation of the parent nuclide A from the daughter B is known or can be estimated from a graph by extrapolation. The activity of the separated portion containing B only at time t is

$$(N_0 - N_B) = N_0 e^{-\lambda_B t}$$

or, in terms of counting rates,

$$(n_0 - n) = n_0 e^{-\lambda_B t}.$$

Let $n = n_1$ at time $t = t_1$,

$$\frac{n_0 - n_1}{n_0} = e^{-\lambda_B t'}.$$

Let $n = n_2$ at time $t = 2t_1$,

$$\frac{n_0 - n_2}{n_0} = e^{-2\lambda_B t_1} = (e^{-\lambda_B t_1})^2$$

$$\frac{n_0 - n_2}{n_0} = \left(\frac{n_0 - n_1}{n_0} \right)^2.$$

Hence
$$n_0 = \frac{n_1^2}{2n_1 - n_2}. \tag{5.3}$$

The value of n_0 is found by using a value of the counting rate n_1 at any time t together with the rate n_2 at the time $2t$. The values of n_1 and n_2 are best read from a graph of n against t. The mean value of n_0 should be found from a number of values of n_1 and n_2. The half-life is found from a graph of n against t; it is equal to the time for the activity to reach half the value of n_0.

Carriers

The weight of an artificially produced radioisotope used in a normal experiment is extremely small, usually much less than a microgramme. It is often impossible to carry out ordinary chemical operations with quantities of this order. For example, if an attempt is made to precipitate such a small amount of a material, it is most unlikely that the solubility product would be exceeded. Even if precipitation did occur, it might be impossible to separate the material by centrifuging or by filtration.

In order to avoid such difficulties it is usual to add a small amount of a stable isotope of the same element in the same chemical form. The stable isotope is referred to as a "carrier", since the radioisotope is always precipitated along with it. If other radioisotopes are present, it may be necessary to add a stable isotope of each of these other elements to prevent them being absorbed on the precipitate.

In the case of some elements, such as technetium and proto-actinium, no stable isotopes are known. In such cases another chemically similar element may be used as a non-isotopic carrier. For example, zirconium ions may be used as a carrier for proto-actinium ions. Ferric hydroxide is used as a carrier for yttrium ions. The main advantage in the use of a non-isotopic carrier is that it can be separated from the radioisotope at a later stage, whereas an isotopic carrier cannot.

Sometimes isotopes are purchased "carrier free"; in such cases the number of inactive atoms may be up to about 100 times the number of active atoms of the element concerned. Other isotopes when purchased may contain some of the unchanged target material or possibly carriers which have been added to simplify separation during the production process.

It was found experimentally that some precipitates would carry small amounts of almost any radionuclide, whilst when other precipitates were formed, a radionuclide would be carried only if it could form an insoluble compound with the ions present. In 1926 Hahn proposed a classification of carrying mechanisms into four main types.

Surface adsorption occurs when a freshly formed precipitate with a large surface area such as ferric or aluminium hydroxide adsorbs ions onto its surface. Such materials can adsorb ions of many types and are sometimes known as "scavengers". The adsorption effect is influenced by the exact conditions of the experiment, e.g. the order of addition of the reagents and the pH. Such factors affect the surface charge on the precipitate and this controls adsorption. An appreciable fraction of the adsorbed material can often be washed off.

In isomorphous replacement the ions of the radionuclide replace ions of the isomorphous carrier material. For example, radium salts are often precipitated with barium salts. The exact conditions of the precipitation have little effect and the carrier nuclide cannot be removed by washing as it is distributed throughout the crystals of the precipitate.

The third type of carrying mechanism, anomalous mixed crystals, is somewhat similar to isomorphous replacement, but occurs when the materials concerned are not isomorphous. For example, ^{212}Pb (thorium B) is carried by barium chloride. The conditions have little effect on the carrying.

There are a few cases known of internal adsorption which appear to be due to the inclusion of colloidal particles of the radionuclide in the precipitate.

Solvent Extraction

The separation of one radionuclide from another can often be accomplished by extracting a suitable compound of the nuclide into an organic solvent. In many cases the extraction can be carried out with carrier-free material, but this does not apply if the compound forms a double molecule (or dimer) in the organic phase. The solvent extraction process has the advantage of taking little time—an important consideration when short-lived materials are being used. The extraction of various chlorides into an organic layer from a hydrochloric acid solution is an especially useful technique.

Ion Exchange

Ion exchange resins are synthetic polymers containing labile ions which are capable of undergoing exchange with ions in the surrounding medium. They fall into two main groups—cation exchange resins and anion exchange resins. The cation exchange resins may contain either a strongly acidic group (usually —SO_3H) or a weakly acid group (usually —COOH), whilst the anion exchange resins often contain an amino group.

A column is partially filled with the exchange resin and a solution containing various ions is poured in at the top. The solution is allowed to flow through the column and the ions are adsorbed on the resin. They are then selectively eluted from the resin by passing suitable solutions through it. Carrier-free solutions of radioisotopes can normally be separated by the ion exchange technique. The method is particularly valuable for use with ions which are not readily separated by chemical methods, e.g. the rare earths.

A burette can conveniently be used to make an ion exchange column. A plug of glass wool is placed at the bottom of the burette and a mixture of the resin and water is poured in. The water level must always be kept above the top of the resin or "channelling" will occur and the solution will not then come into good contact with the resin.

Electro-deposition

If a piece of a suitable metal is added to a solution of a salt of another metal, the latter metal may be deposited on the former and is thus separated from the other metals in the solution. Some radioisotope ions may be conveniently separated in this way.

Preparation of Solid Samples

It is often necessary to filter off a radioactive precipitate so that it may be counted under an end-window Geiger tube. The filtration apparatus shown in Fig. 5.2 or that shown in Fig. 5.3 is very convenient for this purpose. In both types of apparatus a 21 mm diameter filter paper is used and the precipitate is deposited at the centre of it. The apparatus is demountable so that the filter paper and precipitate can be removed with tweezers and placed in one of the standard 22 mm diameter planchets for counting. Precipitates should normally be well washed with water and, if possible, with a small amount of a volatile solvent to reduce the drying time. In the case of short-lived materials, the

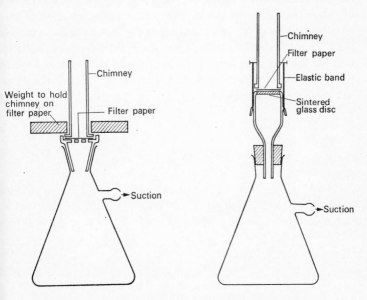

FIGS. 5.2. and 5.3. Alternative designs of filtration equipment.

precipitate must be counted whilst wet. This is undesirable since evaporation may alter the counting efficiency slightly. If the precipitate is to be dried, a 250 W infrared lamp should be placed about a foot above it.

Glass-fibre filter papers are particularly suitable for use in the apparatus of Figs. 5.2 and 5.3, especially if a short-lived isotope is being filtered. They allow much more rapid filtration than a normal type of filter paper and at the same time retain finer particles. They cannot be folded in use, however, and tend to break up if roughly handled. There are three types of Whatman glass-fibre filter papers available at the present time. The general purpose type is coded GF/A, a thicker version is coded GF/B, whilst GF/C is a type with finer fibres.

It is especially important to obtain an even deposit of the solid without any cracks in the surface if a weak beta emitter such as carbon-14 or sulphur-35 is being counted, since a bad surface may produce a counting error exceeding 50%. One of the causes of a defective surface is the use of excessive heat during the drying of the precipitate. When a small volume of a radioactive material is to be gently heated, an infrared lamp should always be used to heat the material from the upper surface downwards, since this prevents "bumping" and the possibility of the material being scattered by the heating.

CHAPTER 6

Some Demonstration Experiments

THE purpose of this chapter is to describe some fairly short experiments; many of them can be performed as demonstrations during elementary lectures on radioactivity or, in some cases, by individual pupils. They do not involve any accurate measurement. All of the experiments described in this chapter are suitable for use in a school.

Experiment 6.1. Becquerel's Discovery

It is often desired to carry out an experiment to illustrate the discovery of radioactivity by Becquerel. The simplest way of doing this involves taking a beta ray shadow photograph of a common object such as a key or a penny. Two methods will be described. The first method employs uranium oxide and involves development about a week after the exposure has begun. The second method involves the use of a sealed source of strontium-90, but development can take place a few minutes after the commencement of the experiment. In either experiment each student may be given a print of the resulting photograph.

1. Using Uranium Oxide

An envelope packed fast X-ray film (such as Ilford Industrial G) is placed in the bottom of a small cardboard box so that it lies flat. Alternatively a fast photographic plate previously wrapped and sealed in black paper may be used. (Boxes used for packing photographic plates are very suitable for use in this experiment.)

A key or other metallic object is fastened by adhesive plastic tap
onto the upper surface of the paper in which the film is wrapped
it should lie flat and close to the film. A thin cardboard tray i
made to fit into the box so that the surface of the tray will b
about $0·5$ cm above the film. About 20–40 g of uranium oxide i
spread evenly on top of the tray. The lid of the box is then re
placed so that it holds the tray in position (Fig. 6.1).

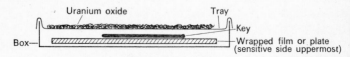

FIG. 6.1. Apparatus for Becquerel's experiment (with lid removed).

After about a week the box is opened in daylight and the tra
and uranium oxide are carefully lifted out. The lecturer can the
give the film or plate to a colleague for developing and fixing
The wet negative may be shown to the audience.

Most uranium containing compounds can be used for thi
experiment, but deliquescent ones such as uranyl nitrate shoul
be avoided if possible. In this experiment it is the beta particle
from the protoactinium-234 (which is in equilibrium with th
uranium) which pass through the cardboard tray and affect th
film. They cannot pass through the key which shows as a ligh
area on the blackened film.

Thorium compounds may also be used in this experiment, bu
a longer exposure (of about 3 weeks) may be required. Thoriun
sulphate is suitable, but thorium nitrate is deliquescent an
should be avoided.

2. *Using ^{90}Sr Foil*

In this experiment a fast envelope wrapped X-ray film i
placed·in an empty balance case (which provides reasonabl
shielding from beta radiation) and a key or other object is place
on the film. A piece of strontium-90 foil is withdrawn from it

shielding and quickly placed on a suitable support a few centimetres above the film. The balance case is closed and left for about 1–5 min. The foil is then replaced in its normal shielding and the film is given to a colleague to be developed and fixed. The wet negative can be shown to the audience within about 10 min.

The ^{90}Sr foil recommended for this experiment is that obtainable from the Radiochemical Centre, Amersham, under the catalogue number SIM3; it contains about 75 μcurie of ^{90}Sr per cm of its length. A convenient length is about 5 cm. Such a beta source gives a high dose rate (of the order of 100 mrad/hr at 1 ft) and great care must therefore be taken to ensure that it is suitably handled. The dose rate from the active face of the foil is several times that from the rear surface. The face of the foil should therefore be kept pointing downwards away from the eyes. Forceps at least 1 ft in length should be used to manipulate this source.

Experiment 6.2. Distinction between
Alpha, Beta and Gamma Radiation

A method of illustrating the existence of three types of radiation is shown in many textbooks by the type of diagram of Fig. 6.2. A collimated source which emits all three types of radiation is

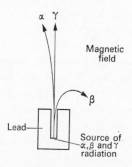

FIG. 6.2. Deflection of alpha and beta rays in a magnetic field.

employed. The positively charged alpha radiation is deflected slightly in one direction by the magnetic field, whilst the beta particles are deflected to a much greater extent in the opposite direction, since they are much lighter than alpha particles and have an opposite charge. The gamma rays pass through the magnetic field undeflected, as they have no charge.

This type of experiment appears very satisfactory in theory, but is almost impossible to carry out in practice. If a magnetic field is employed which will produce the smallest detectable deflection of the alpha particles, the beta particles will be deflected into the side of the collimating tube before they even emerge from it. The experiment would in any case have to be performed in a vacuum or under reduced pressure to increase the path length of the alpha particles.

It is felt that a satisfactory demonstration of the difference between alpha, beta and gamma radiation can be shown by absorption experiments, although these are admittedly not so satisfactory from the theoretical point of view. They would not distinguish a low-energy beta emitter from an alpha emitter.

Small sealed sources of a pure alpha, a pure beta and a gamma emitter are required. The alpha emitter is first placed above an end-window Geiger tube so that counts are recorded. A piece of paper is then placed between the source and the tube window. The counting rate should fall to the background rate showing that alpha radiation cannot pass through paper. By withdrawing the source from the tube window one can also show that alpha particles cannot pass through more than a few centimetres of air. If the range in air is to be estimated, allowance must be made for the thickness of the tube window. Alternatively a semiconductor dector could be used. A source of about $0 \cdot 1$–1 μcurie of ^{241}Am or ^{239}Pu is suitable for this experiment.

The same procedure is then repeated with a beta emitter. The insertion of the paper will leave the counting rate almost unchanged. Cardboard and aluminium sheets may be tried until an aluminium sheet is found which will cut off most of the beta radiation.

When a gamma emitter is used, the counting rate will be little affected by the insertion of an aluminium absorber of normal thickness. Lead absorbers will make an appreciable difference. A good way of demonstrating the penetrating properties of gamma radiation involves placing a source of about 10 μcurie of cobalt-60 in a lead pot of 1 in. wall thickness and noting the fall in the counting rate.

The rapidity with which the counting rate decreases with source to Geiger tube distance can usefully be shown when the gamma source is being used.

A student with a luminous watch may be asked to put it near the Geiger tube window and ascertain by the use of absorbers whether alpha, beta or gamma particles are being emitted from the face. The back of the watch should also be tried. Some very rough estimate of the activity may be made by comparison with sources whose strength is approximately known.

After it has been shown that there is more than one type of radiation, the penetrating properties of beta and gamma radiation of various energies may be quickly demonstrated. The beta particles from ^{90}Sr (which is in equilibrium with its decay product, ^{90}Y) will penetrate a greater thickness of aluminium than those from ^{204}Tl and these in turn will penetrate a greater thickness than those from ^{14}C or ^{35}S.

Similarly it can be shown that gamma radiation from cobalt-60 will be reduced in intensity by a smaller factor when it penetrates a given thickness of lead than the gamma radiation from caesium-137.

Experiment 6.3. Deflection of Beta Particles in a Magnetic Field

If a collimated source of beta particles is available, it is easy to show that the particles are deflected in a magnetic field and that the direction of deflection changes with the direction of the field. A Geiger tube may be used as the detector. Suitable small collimated sources (such as 10 μcurie of ^{90}Sr) are now available commercially for this experiment. They are included in some educational kits. The magnetic field should have a fairly high value. Most halogen quenched Geiger tubes employ a chrome iron cathode and some trouble may arise owing to the attraction between this and the magnet.

It is probably wise to ask students to apply the left-hand motor rule to the bending of beta radiation in a magnetic field and hence to deduce the polarity of the charge of the beta particles.

Experiment 6.4. Backscatter

If a source of about 10 μcuries of a beta emitter is placed at the side of a Geiger tube as in Fig. 6.3 so that no particles can

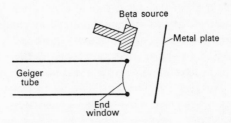

FIG. 6.3. Demonstration of beta particle backscattering.

enter the tube window, the count rate will increase considerably when a sheet of metal is placed in the position shown. An estimate may be made of the dependence of the counting rate on the type of metal used as a reflector or on the thickness of a film of paint on the metal surface.

Experiment 6.5. Activity of Potassium Salts

Many people tend to think of radioactivity as being a very uncommon phenomenon which concerns only scientists and industrialists. A short demonstration of the activity of potassium salts shows that it is a common phenomenon of everyday life. One can also mention that the amount of potassium in an average human being gives rise to about 10^6 disintegrations/min, contributing a dose of the order of 20 mrad/year.

The beta particles from potassium-40 have an energy of $1 \cdot 325$ MeV and are therefore readily detected by a liquid counter. In a 5 ml MX142 liquid sample Geiger tube, a saturated solution of potassium chloride provides a counting rate of about 55 counts/min; this figure includes a background counting rate of about 10 counts/min. In the more sensitive MX124/01 tube, the figure is about 140 counts/min including the background of about 12 counts/min. Although the solubility of potassium iodide in moles per litre is about $1 \cdot 5$ times that of potassium chloride, the resulting solution is denser. A saturated solution of potassium iodide provides about 60 counts/min in an MX142 tube and about 160 counts/min in an MX124/01 tube (including the background counting rates). If $0 \cdot 3$ g of solid potassium chloride is placed under an MX123 end-window counter, a net sample counting rate of about 30 counts/min is obtained.

Experiment 6.6. Cloud Chambers

The main value of a cloud chamber is that a pictorial representation of the paths taken by the ionising particles a fraction of a second earlier is provided. The ions formed by the particles are made visible by the condensation of drops of water on them. The chamber must be well illuminated from the side. There are two types of cloud chamber, namely the expansion type and the diffusion type.

In the expansion cloud chamber an enclosed gas is saturated with vapour (usually water or alcohol or a mixture of both) and is quickly cooled by adiabatic expansion so that the gas becomes supersaturated. In the type of equipment often used in schools, a pump resembling a bicycle pump may be used to produce the expansion. Condensation occurs preferentially on ions. The air inside the chamber should be reasonably dust free and stray ions must be removed by the application of an electric field of the order of 100 V/cm. After the chamber has been first assembled, it will probably be necessary to wait for a few minutes to enable the liquid to come into equilibrium with the vapour. The expansion ratio must be carefully chosen if the formation of a general mist in the chamber is to be avoided. The tracks are usually visible for a time of rather less than a second.

Solid carbon dioxide is required for cooling the base of diffusion cloud chambers. The region of supersaturation is formed as a saturated organic vapour diffuses downwards into the colder regions. The working volume of the diffusion cloud chamber is continuously sensitive, whereas the expansion cloud chamber is sensitive only for a fraction of a second at the end of each expansion. The diffusion chamber takes about a quarter of an hour to become sensitive, but the sensitive region does not reach its full depth for about another quarter of an hour.

Alpha particles produce dense fog droplets containing thousands of drops per centimetre of the track, whilst beta particles produce much less noticeable tracks. Gamma rays do not produce any clear track. For demonstrations at school level an alpha source is therefore the most suitable. An activity of about $0 \cdot 1$ μcurie is about optimum. Although many measurements can be made with cloud chambers, the only one which is really suitable for school level is the measurement of the distance an alpha particle will travel in air. Diffusion cloud chambers will detect particles in the natural background. If thoron is introduced into a diffusion cloud chamber, some V-shaped tracks are seen. These are due to the decay of a thoron atom being quickly followed by the decay of the short-lived thorium A. (See Plates N and O.)

Experiment 6.7. Relative Ionising Power of Alpha, Beta and Gamma Radiations

The relative number of ions formed by sources of alpha, beta and gamma radiation in a limited volume of air can be conveniently estimated by the use of an ion chamber of the type shown in Fig. 2.12 (p. 41). The dosimeter should first be charged to a potential such that the indicator is somewhat beyond the

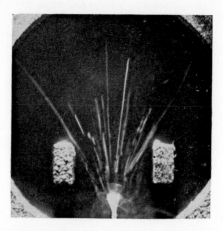

PLATE N. Tracks of alpha particles in the Taylor diffusion cloud chamber. (By courtesy of B. Taylor Esq. and Griffin & George Ltd.)

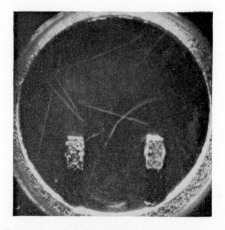

PLATE O. Tracks due to alpha particles from thoron. The V-shaped track is due to the emission of an alpha particle from thoron followed almost immediately by the emission of an alpha particle from the short-lived daughter product ^{216}Po. A Taylor diffusion cloud chamber was employed. (By courtesy of B. Taylor Esq. and Griffin & George Ltd.)

zero mark (i.e. off the scale). A sealed source of about $0 \cdot 1$ μcurie of an alpha emitter is placed inside the chamber. A stop-watch is started as the indicator passes the zero mark and is stopped when it passes the point of full scale reading. The time interval (of the order of a minute) and the source strength are noted.

The experiment is repeated using a beta source of 1–10 μcurie. Owing to the relatively low ionising power of gamma radiation, a somewhat stronger source is required when this type of radiation is being examined. A 100 μcurie source will give a full-scale deflection in about 10 min.

In each case the time taken to obtain a full-scale deflection per microcurie of the isotope used should be found. The times taken by the beta and gamma radiation to discharge the electroscope relative to that taken by the alpha radiation of the same source strength is found. A typical result is 1:40:40,000 for alpha:beta: gamma. Such a result can obviously only be very approximate indeed, since geometrical differences between the various cases are not taken into account. Nevertheless, this experiment does give some idea of the order of magnitudes involved.

Experiment 6.8. Scintillations

A number of commercial spinthariscopes are available. They consist of a zinc sulphide screen and a fraction of a microcurie of an alpha emitter (often radium) sealed into a box which contains a viewing lens. It is essential for students to become dark adapted over a period of about 10 min or they will not be able to see the weak scintillations. Those who attempt to count scintillations visually, even at a low recurrence rate, will readily appreciate the difficulties which the early experimenters met.

The activated zinc sulphide which is used in this type of instrument will show phosphorescence for some time after it has been exposed to light. It should therefore be kept in darkness for a short time immediately before use. Students can conveniently carry out this experiment whilst they are developing a film in a dark room.

Experiment 6.9. Dose Rate Measurements

It is instructive to carry out dose rate calculations of the type discussed in Chapter 4 for a source which one has available and then to compare the measured and calculated dose rates. Reasonable accuracy cannot be expected unless the source to detector distance is $1\frac{1}{2}$–2 ft, since errors in distance measurement will be appreciable at smaller distances; in addition the radiation field at the detector will not be reasonably uniform if the source to detector distance is small. A gamma source of at least 100 μcurie or preferably 1 mcurie is therefore desirable for use in this experiment. The integrated dose may also be measured by a pocket dosimeter, but a source of a similar strength is required for this.

Experiment 6.10. The Spark Counter

One form of spark counter consists of a wire about 5 cm in length which is held taut by supports about 2 mm above a metal base. A potential of a few kilovolts should be applied between the wire and the metal base via a series safety resistor of about 2 MΩ. When a weak alpha source is held just above the wire facing downwards, sparking will occur at intervals of the order of a second. The range of the alpha particles in air can be roughly estimated by raising the alpha source until the sparking ceases. The sparking is, of course, initiated by the ions formed by the alpha particles. A source of about 5 μcurie is ideal. Beta and gamma radiation do not normally produce any effect.

Experiment 6.11. Half-life Experiments

The experiments for the separation of the short-lived ^{234m}Pa which will be discussed in detail in the next chapter are very suitable for use in a lecture demonstration. However, the decay of thoron is, perhaps, even more suitable, since one does not have to explain details of a separation process. The thoron is obtained, mixed with air, from about 10 g of thorium hydroxide sewn in a felt container; the latter is placed in a plastic bottle fitted with an outlet tube. The gas passes through the felt into the bottle and is expelled by squeezing the latter. Solid particles cannot pass through the felt filter.

One method for determining the half-life of thoron involves the use of an ionisation chamber, a valve amplifier and a large-scale moving-coil meter (Fig. 6.4). A power unit to supply a potential of about 2 kV is also required. When a small amount of thoron gas is placed in the ionisation chamber, a very small current passes through the safety resistor R (about 1 MΩ) and through the ionised gas into the amplifier. The meter deflection

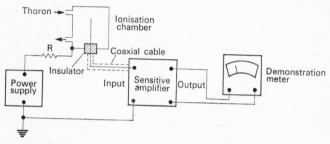

FIG. 6.4. Apparatus for demonstrating the decay of thoron.

is proportional to the current passing through the ionisation chamber. This current varies with the activity of the gas, but is typically of the order of 10^{-10} to 10^{-11} A. The resistor R is often incorporated inside the power supply.

The current passing through the ionisation chamber is equal to the charge produced per unit time by the alpha particles formed by the decay of thoron and thorium A. (The activity of thorium B and further decay products which are formed as a result of the decay of thorium A is negligible, since the half-life of thorium B is very much greater than that of thoron.) Although the activity being measured is the total activity due to thoron and thorium A, the half-life of the latter is so short that the meter reading is proportional to the instantaneous activity of the thoron.

In a simple demonstration, the time taken for the meter reading to fall to half its initial value may be measured. Alternatively a graph of $\log_{10}$(meter reading) against time may be plotted in order to obtain a more accurate value of the half-life. Suitable apparatus is commercially available.

An alternative demonstration experiment to determine the half-life of thoron involves the use of a pulse electroscope, an ionisation chamber and a power supply of 2–4 kV (Fig. 6.5). An image of the leaf may be projected for the audience to see. When

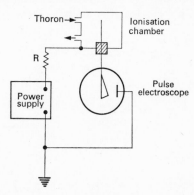

FIG. 6.5. Alternative apparatus for determining the half-life of thoron.

thoron is placed in the ionisation chamber, charge passes to the electroscope leaf. As the deflection increases, a point will be reached at which the leaf touches the side electrode and is discharged. The rate at which the leaf touches the side electrode is proportional to the ionisation current and hence to the activity.

Unfortunately the instantaneous rate of pulsing of the leaf cannot be measured. The time at which the leaf is first discharged may be taken as zero and the time of each subsequent discharge noted. If the number of a discharge n is plotted against the time at which the discharge occurred, a graph of the form

$$\frac{n_0 - n}{n_0} = e^{-\lambda t}$$

is obtained, where λ is the radioactive constant of thoron and n_0 is the number of discharges (including any fractional discharges) which would have been obtained if the experiment had been prolonged until the activity had decayed to zero. The form of this equation is similar to that of the growth curve of a short-lived daughter product in a specimen of a long-lived parent; the half-life can thus be found by one of the methods discussed in Chapter 5 for growth curves. For example, the value of n_0 can be calculated from the equation

$$n_0 = \frac{n_1^2}{2n_1 - n_2},$$

where n_1 is the value of n after any time t and n_2 is its value after a time $2t$. This equation is analogous to eqn. (5.3) and may be derived in a similar way. The half-life of thoron is the time taken for the number of pulses to reach a value of $n_0/2$.

A method which is more suitable for the determination of the half-life of thoron by an individual student will be discussed in Chapter 7.

Experiment 6.12. Alpha Particle Range

A pulse electroscope may be used to show that alpha particles ionise the air through which they are passing and to carry out some measurements on alpha particle ranges.

The type of apparatus which may be employed is shown in Fig. 6.6. An ionisation chamber fitted with a grid is employed. As an alpha particle source is brought near to the grid, some of the alpha particles pass through it, thus forming ions inside the chamber. These ions are collected by the electrodes and form a current which is detected by the electroscope. Any ions formed outside the chamber will be screened from the electric field by the grid and will not be collected. As the source is moved away from the grid, a point will be reached at which no current is detected. The source to grid distance is then equal to the range of the alpha particles in air. As the source is moved away from the grid, some reduction in the rate of pulsing will be noticed before the current falls to zero. This is due to the inverse square law effect, the reduction in the fraction of the total number of ions formed inside the chamber by an alpha particle and the fact that some particles are emitted from the source with a smaller energy than others owing to self-absorption.

If the source is brought very near to the grid and one or more very thin absorbers are placed in between the source and the grid, the proportion of alpha particles which penetrate the

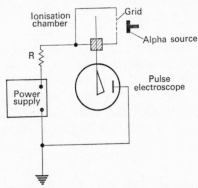

FIG. 6.6. Determination of alpha particle range.

absorber can be estimated. Layers of very thin aluminium foil (about 0·0003 cm in thickness) may be used as absorbers or alternatively very thin paper (e.g. cigarette paper) may be employed; ordinary paper will completely absorb alpha particles of normal energies. A similar experiment may be carried out using a semiconductor detector.

Experiment 6.13. Bremsstrahlung Production

Bremsstrahlung is the fairly soft electromagnetic radiation produced when beta particles strike matter. The amount of bremsstrahlung produced is much greater if the material with which the beta particles interact contains heavy atoms than if only light atoms are present. It is easier to show the presence of bremsstrahlung with a scintillation detector than with a Geiger tube, since the efficiency of the latter for the detection of this type of radiation is very low. A Geiger tube may, however, be used in the following way to show the production of bremsstrahlung. The experiment also shows the importance of placing a shielding material containing only light nuclei around a strong beta source in order to minimise bremsstrahlung production.

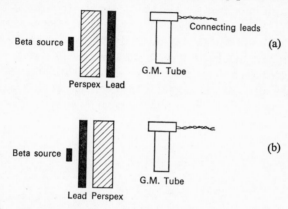

FIG. 6.7. Demonstration of bremsstrahlung production. The counting rate in (b) is greater than in (a).

A sheet of perspex (or a sheet of another light material) and a sheet of lead are placed between a Geiger tube and a beta source as shown in Fig. 6.7. The beta source may have a strength of about 100 μcurie. The counting rate is first found with the perspex nearest to the source as in Fig. 6.7a and then with the lead nearest the source as in Fig. 6.7b. In the first case the beta particles are absorbed in the perspex before they reach the lead and little bremsstrahlung is produced. Although the total absorber thickness is constant, the counting rate is higher in the second case (Fig. 6.7b), since the bremsstrahlung produced in the lead can easily pass through the perspex.

The source used in this experiment should preferably consist of a suitable beta emitter sealed in a plastic container having a thin window of a plastic sheet. Open sources cause contamination dangers, whilst the use of a source sealed in metal will result in the production of additional bremsstrahlung as the beta particles strike the metal. It has been found, however, that a few centimetres of the Amersham type SIM3 metal foil containing strontium-90 can be used in this experiment, the counting rate with the arrangement of Fig. 6.7b being about twice that with Fig. 6.7a. A plastic mounted source provides a higher ratio of counting rates.

The thickness of the perspex and of the lead sheets used in this experiment should be at least great enough to absorb all of the beta particles striking them. In the case of a strontium-90 source, the perspex sheet may have a thickness of about 2 cm and the lead sheet a thickness of about 3 g/cm^2.

CHAPTER 7

Experiments
Using Naturally Occurring Radioisotopes

IN THIS chapter it is shown that a very wide range of experimental work can be carried out using naturally occurring nuclides together with simple equipment. A few of the experiments are fairly long, but these should be useful for students in residential schools and for students in colleges of education who are preparing a "special study" in the subject, etc. The radiotoxicity of the materials used is very low and it is not normally necessary for a lecturer or teacher to be present in the room when such experiments are being performed by older pupils.

Experiment 7.1. The Characteristics of a Geiger Tube

The plotting of the characteristic of a Geiger tube does not merely provide a useful student exercise; it also enables the operation of a tube to be checked. This is especially important with organically quenched tubes, since their characteristics deteriorate with age.

A stable reference source is required. The preparation of a suitable source from uranium oxide is described, but the experiment may also be performed with a source of an artificially produced nuclide of suitable activity.

The Source

In order to obtain reasonable statistical accuracy in an hour or so, a source should be used which will provide a counting rate of the order of 10,000 counts/min. The specific activities of naturally occurring compounds except those containing uranium or thorium are too low for this counting rate to be developed. The most convenient material for use with an end window tube is undoubtedly a uranium compound. The alpha particles from the ^{238}U and the weak beta particles from the ^{234}Th may be filtered off with a thin absorber so that only the energetic beta particles from ^{234m}Pa are detected. Deliquescent compounds of uranium should obviously be avoided. The uranium compound chosen should not have been treated chemically within the previous 9 months or the amount of ^{234}Th and ^{234m}Pa present may not be in equilibrium with the ^{238}U, in which case the activity of the source will change somewhat with time. The black uranium oxide, U_3O_8, is very suitable for this experiment.

A very weak solution of perspex in a volatile solvent such as acetone or chloroform is mixed with about 2 g of uranium oxide and stirred with a glass rod. A small amount of the slurry is transferred to a planchet and evaporated to dryness under an infrared lamp. An even deposit will be obtainable if the solvent is not evaporated too quickly. A little more of the slurry is then added and the material is again evaporated to dryness. This process is continued until the source will give a counting rate of about 10,000–15,000 counts/min through an aluminium absorber of about 35 mg/cm^2. The perspex serves to cement the particles of the oxide in position.

A circular piece of aluminium foil of about 35 mg/cm^2 may be cemented onto the top of the source with araldite. The source should be warmed under an infrared lamp so that this adhesive sets within a reasonably short time.

Characteristics of the Tube

The Geiger tube is connected to a scaler and the source placed in position under the end window. The potential applied to the tube is slowly increased until the scaler just commences to count. It is then counted for a period of between 2 and 4 min. The applied potential is increased in steps of 20–25 V and the counting rate found at each voltage. The process is repeated until the potential is about 250 V above the starting potential or until an appreciable increase in the counting rate occurs (showing that the end of the plateau has been passed).

A graph of counting rate against the applied voltage is plotted (Fig. 2.3) (p. 20). No correction for resolving time or for background counts need be made. In general it will not be very easy to plot parts of the curve other than the plateau region accurately, but these other parts are relatively unimportant.

The plateau should extend for at least 100 V in a halogen quenched tube or at least 150 V in an organically quenched tube. The slope of the plateau should be found. It may be expressed in terms of the fractional change in the counting rate per 100 V change in applied potential, this being equal to the percentage change in counting rate per volt change in potential; it is equal to

$$\frac{\triangle N}{\triangle V} \times \frac{100}{N} \text{ per cent per volt,}$$

where $\triangle N/\triangle V =$ slope of the plateau and $N =$ counting rate at the working voltage.

Further Comments

The plateau of a liquid sample tube may be plotted by using a solution of thorium nitrate (about 25%) or a rather weaker solution of uranyl nitrate.

Geiger tubes should be regularly checked to ensure that their characteristic is satisfactory, but it is not necessary to plot the whole of the characteristic. One method of quickly checking the performance of a Geiger tube involves the measurement of the counting rate of a standard source at a potential of 25 V below and 75 V above the working voltage over at least 20,000 counts each. If these rates differ by more than about 10%, the tube is not very satisfactory for accurate work.

Experiment 7.2. Geiger Pulse Amplitude and Duration

In this experiment an end-window halogen quenched Geiger tube is employed in the circuit of Fig. 7.1. A fairly thick uranium oxide source is brought near to the window and the H.T. + potential applied to the Geiger tube is adjusted to about the recommended operating value. The oscilloscope time base is set to the "triggered" position and the sweep speed is adjusted so that the pulse shown on the screen is spread over a reasonably large part of the X axis.

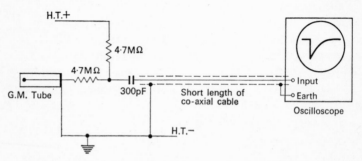

FIG. 7.1. A circuit for the examination of Geiger tube output pulses.

It will be found that the pulse height remains steady. The source emits alpha, beta and gamma radiation and therefore the pulse amplitude must be independent of the type of radiation producing the ionization. If the counting rate is high, however, an appreciable number of pulses will occur immediately after the preceding pulse; such pulses will have a reduced amplitude.

It is instructive to measure the pulse height at various values of the applied potential and to plot a graph showing the relationship between these quantities. The total charge passing through the tube per pulse may also be estimated from the pulse shape and the value of the anode resistor employed. If the output from the Geiger tube is connected both to the oscilloscope and to a scaler, it can be shown that at low applied potentials pulses are present at the oscilloscope which are too small to operate the scaler.

Experiment 7.3. The Statistics of Counting

The uranium oxide source prepared in experiment 7.1 or any other source giving a similar counting rate may be used in this experiment. All counts should be recorded with the source in the same position. The counting equipment must be allowed to warm up fully before any counts are taken.

The source should be counted for at least twenty-five 1 min periods, but, if enough time is available, it is better to count it for forty or fifty 1 min periods. If a greater number of results is obtained, better agreement with the theory is probable. In this experiment it is especially important that the timing should be carried out very accurately. No correction for resolving time losses or for the background counting rate need be made.

The mean counting rate is found from the results; it will be denoted as $\overline{N}$. A comparison between the results and the theory is made in the following way.

(i) The standard deviation σ is found from the relationship

$$\sigma = \sqrt{\left(\frac{\Sigma (d)^2}{n - 1}\right)},$$

where $n =$ the number of counting periods, $d =$ the deviation or difference between any count and the mean value $\overline{N}$, Σ is the normal summation sign. The standard deviation should be of about the same value as $\sqrt{\overline{N}}$.

(ii) The percentage of counts whose deviation exceeds the standard deviation is found. It should be approximately 32%.

(iii) The percentage of counts whose deviation exceeds the probable error $(= 0 \cdot 675 \, \sigma)$ should be found. This will normally be about 50%.

(iv) If the percentage of counts whose deviation exceeds twice the standard deviation is found, it should be about 5%.

(v) A histogram may be drawn showing the relative frequency with which counts occur within certain ranges of values.

Experiment 7.4. Determination
as to whether a Solid is Radioactive

The instructor should prepare a few samples, some of which consist of pure sodium chloride and some of which are a mixture of sodium and potassium chlorides. The latter are, of course, weakly active. About 1 part of potassium chloride in 10 parts of sodium chloride is suitable.

The samples should be counted for a reasonably short time, say 10 min, and the background count taken over the same period.

Let the total (sample plus background) counts obtained be N_T counts in 10 minutes.

Let the background counts obtained in 10 min be N_B. The corresponding standard deviations σ_T and σ_B are $\sqrt{N_T}$ and $\sqrt{N_B}$. The net sample counting rate is $N_S = N_T - N_B$ and the standard deviation of N_S is $\sigma_S = \sqrt{(N_T + N_B)}$ [from eqn. (2.1)].

In order to be able to state which samples show a measurable activity, one must select a "confidence level". For example, if one decides that it will not matter if there is a chance of 1 in 40 that a sample one states is active is really inactive, one sets a criterion for activity as $N_T - N_B > 2\sqrt{(N_T + N_B)}$. (Although there is a chance of about 1 in 20 that the deviation exceeds twice the standard deviation, in this case we are likely to state that an active material is inactive only if the statistical error leads to a low value of N_S. Low and high deviations occur with about equal frequency. Hence there is a chance of about 1 in 40 that the deviation is negative and exceeds twice the standard deviation.)

Obviously one cannot formulate a similar criterion for deciding whether a material is inactive, since it may have a very low activity. If the above criterion for activity is not satisfied, one can either count for a longer period or accept a lower confidence level. For example, if $N_T - N_B > \sqrt{(N_T + N_B)}$ there is a chance of about 1 in 6 that the material is not active.

Counting rates are, of course, so low in this type of experiment that the correction for lost counts due to the finite resolving time is negligible. The same type of experiment could be carried out with a liquid sample Geiger tube using a solution of potassium chloride as the active material and sodium chloride or water as the inactive material.

Experiment 7.5. External Beta Absorption Curves

The main purpose of plotting beta absorption curves is usually to enable the maximum energy of the emitted beta particles to be determined in order to identify the isotope concerned.

In this experiment a uranium oxide source is prepared as in experiment 7.1, but the thickness of the oxide is limited to about 10 mg/cm² and no aluminium foil is cemented to the top of the source. The source is placed under an end-window counter where it provides a counting rate of about 3000 counts/min. It is counted for periods of 1 or 2 min using aluminium absorbers of increasing thickness. As the counting rate decreases, longer counting times will be required. About six counts should be taken in the range 0–35 mg/cm² and then in steps of 50–100 mg/cm² until a thickness of about 1200 mg/cm² has been reached. The absorbers should be placed as close as possible to the tube window.

If the resolving time is known, corrections are made for lost counts. The background is subtracted. A graph of $\log_{10}$ (corrected counts per minute) is plotted against the absorber thickness, this being most conveniently done on semilogarithmic graph paper. The graph should be fairly linear at absorber thicknesses exceeding about 30 mg/cm². This part of the curve is due to the absorption of beta particles from ²³⁴ᵐPa, whilst the initial rapid fall is due to the low-energy beta particles from ²³⁴Th together with some alpha particles from the uranium isotopes (Fig. 2.8) (p. 35). The main part of the graph due to beta particles from ²³⁴Pa may be extrapolated back to zero absorber thickness in order to ascertain the counting rate due to ^{234}Pa alone without any absorber.

If the experiment is repeated using a much thicker source (about 200 mg/cm^2), the whole curve will be fairly linear. This is because only a very small proportion of the low-energy beta particles from ^{234}Th can escape from the thick source and their effect on the counting rate is completely obscured by the much larger number of energetic beta particles from the ^{234m}Pa.

The "half-thickness" is the thickness of absorber required to reduce the counting rate to one-half of that when no absorber is present. The half-thickness for ^{234m}Pa may be estimated from the fairly straight part of the absorption curve, taking the count rate at zero thickness as the point where the extrapolated curve meets the y axis. The measured value of the half-thickness may be used to estimate the maximum energy of the ^{234m}Pa beta particles using the approximate formula: half-thickness in mg/cm$^2 = 46\ E^{3/2}$, where E is the maximum energy of the beta particles in megaelectron volts.

The absorption coefficient for ^{234m}Pa beta particles in aluminium may be estimated from the slope of the main part of the graph [refer to eqn. (1.6)].

Further Comments

There is appreciable self-absorption in any uranium oxide source. It is preferable to separate ^{234}Th by one of the methods to be discussed in a later experiment and to use this as a source of small weight.

Ideally an allowance should be made for the absorption which occurs in the Geiger tube window and in the air between the source and the Geiger tube. In the case of fairly energetic beta particles such as those from ^{234m}Pa, however, these effects are small when a Geiger tube with a thin mica end window is used. Allowance can easily be made for these effects by extrapolating the main linear part of the graph slightly beyond the y axis. If the total thickness of air plus the Geiger tube window is x mg/cm^2, the curve should be extrapolated back to $-x$ mg/cm² to obtain the count rate with zero absorber thickness.

Experiment 7.6. Self-absorption in a Beta Emitter

In this experiment various amounts of a finely powdered uranium compound such as U_3O_8 are successively weighed into a fairly deep planchet and counted for periods of 1 min. An absorber of about 35 mg/cm² is placed between the source and the Geiger tube so that only the beta radiation from ^{234m}Pa is counted. A range of weights of uranium oxide from about 50 mg up to about 2–4 g can be used in a 22 mm diameter planchet. The material should always be tapped down evenly in the planchet before it is counted. The area of the source is measured.

The counting rate is plotted against the source thickness in mg/cm². Estimate what the counting rate would have been per gramme of the oxide if no self-absorption had been present. Estimate also the minimum thickness for the condition of "infinite thickness" to be attained; compare this with the range of the particles estimated from the results of the previous experiment. Find the self-weakening half-thickness and, using the results of the previous experiment, express this in terms of the external absorption half-thickness.

Calculate the self-absorption factor s from your results for various thicknesses and make a correction chart for self-absorption losses by plotting s against the source thickness. Using the value for the absorption coefficient found in experiment 7.5, calculate s for various thicknesses using eqn. (2.3) and compare the calculated values with those obtained experimentally.

Estimate the efficiency of your counting arrangement from the specific activity of uranium oxide (calculated from the half-life of uranium and Avogadro's number). Use the results of experiment 7.5 to allow for the absorber thickness. Owing to the presence of the absorber, only the activity of ^{234m}Pa need be considered; this is, of course, equal to the activity of the uranium provided radioactive equilibrium has been attained.

Experiment 7.7. Self-absorption in a Solution

The effects of self-absorption can also be investigated by the use of an aqueous solution of uranyl nitrate. The solution to be counted is placed in a container with a flat base and of constant horizontal cross-section. The diameter and the height of this container should each be about 3 cm. A suitable container may be made by cutting off the top portion of a weighing bottle. It is supported under the end window of a Geiger tube.

The variation in the counting rate with the volume of a source of constant total activity may first be found in the following way. 2 ml of a 20% solution of uranyl nitrate is placed in the container and counted. The counting is then repeated after 2 ml of water have been added, care being taken that the solution is thoroughly mixed. Further counts are taken after the addition of further known amounts of water. The corrected counting rate is plotted against the total volume.

It is also instructive to carry out an experiment with an increasing volume of a solution of constant specific activity. A known volume of a 20% solution of uranyl nitrate is placed in the container and counted. Further quantities of the same solution are added and the counting rate is plotted against the volume of the solution in the container.

If enough time is available, a further experiment may be carried out by counting the same volume of solutions of various concentrations. A graph of the counting rate against concentration may be plotted; note whether the increased density of the solution at high concentrations affects the linearity of the graph.

This experiment is very useful for illustrating the principles of self-absorption, but the first two parts of the experiment cannot be expected to provide accurate results. As the volume increases, the surface of the liquid comes nearer to the Geiger tube window. In order to minimise errors due to this effect, the surface of the liquid being counted should not be allowed to come very near to the window of the tube.

Experiment 7.8. The Separation
of ^{234m}Pa by Solvent Extraction

The separation of ^{234m}Pa by solvent extraction and the determination of its half-life is a very convenient student experiment which can be carried out in quite a short time. If enough time is available, however, the experiment may be considerably extended.

The separation is based on the fact that protoactinium forms a chloro-complex at high concentrations of hydrochloric acid. This complex may be extracted with a suitable organic solvent and counted in a liquid sample tube. About 95% of the isotope is extracted. It has a short half-life and therefore all equipment should be ready before the commencement of the experiment.

The quantities given below are suitable for use with a 10 ml liquid sample tube; if a 5 ml plug-in liquid sample Geiger tube is employed, the quantities should be halved. Dissolve 1–1·5 g of uranyl nitrate crystals in about 10 ml of 8 N hydrochloric acid (3 parts of concentrated hydrochloric acid to 1 part of water). The liquids must be measured with a safety pipette. Pour the mixture into a separating funnel and add 10 ml of iso-butylmethyl ketone, amyl acetate or a similar organic solvent. Shake vigorously for half a minute. As soon as the liquids have started to separate, start running the lower acid layer into a small bottle. Ensure that the last drops of this layer are removed. Pour the upper organic layer from the top of the separating funnel into a liquid sample tube.

The counting should be started as soon as the tube is full. Count for a period of 20 sec followed by an interval of 10 sec for recording the counting rate obtained and resetting the scaler to zero. Continue counting for periods of 20 sec with 10 sec intervals between the counting periods until little further decrease in the counting rate occurs (about 10 min after the commencement of counting). The stop-watch is started at the beginning of the first count and should not be stopped until the counting has been completed. About 20 min after the start of the counting, count for a single period of 3 min to find the background due to activity other than ^{234m}Pa which passed into the organic layer. Use this value as the background when correcting the count rates.

The organic layer may be poured into the bottle containing the aqueous layer for future use. It is only necessary to shake the mixture in a separating funnel and to separate the layers when repeating the experiment. The Geiger tube should be cleaned with concentrated hydrochloric acid and checked for contamination.

Plot a graph of $\log_{10}$ (corrected counting rate) against time as described in Chapter 5 and hence find the half-life of ^{234m}Pa.

Further Comments

About one-third of the uranium is extracted into the organic layer, since it forms a similar complex to that formed by the protoactinium. Thorium does not form this type of compound. The organic layer is coloured yellow by the presence of the uranium, but the alpha particles from it are not detected since they cannot pass through the walls of the tube. ^{234}Th remains in the acid layer. The amount of it formed during the course of the experiment in the organic layer is negligible, since it has a half-life of $24\cdot1$ days. Thus only the ^{234m}Pa which is extracted is counted.

No separation is perfect, and a small amount of ^{234}Th will, of course, pass into the organic layer. In practice, however, it is found that an initial counting rate of the order of 20,000 counts/min in an MX124/01 tube or about 4000 counts/min in an MX142 tube can be obtained, whilst the "background" rate due to the extracted ^{234}Th is typically about 100 counts/min in an MX124/01 tube. This background can, however, be reduced to the normal background rate for the tube by quickly washing the separated organic layer with 8 N hydrochloric acid and separating again before counting. In this case 10 ml of 8 N hydrochloric acid should be placed ready for use in the second separating funnel before the first separation is carried out. Although this process removes virtually all of the ^{234}Th from the organic layer, the operation takes about a minute and the ^{234m}Pa is decaying during this time. Washing the organic layer thus reduces the maximum initial counting rate by a factor of about 2. For this reason it is very doubtful as to whether it is worth while to wash the organic layer.

A ratemeter may be employed instead of a scaler, but a reasonably short time constant should then be selected (about 5 sec).

Specimen Results for ^{234m}Pa Half-life

The Geiger tube used was an MX124/01 and the resolving time of the system was 400 μsec. One gramme of uranyl nitrate was used with 10 ml of 8 N hydrochloric acid and 10 ml of iso-butyl-methyl ketone. The times shown in the left-hand column of Table 7.1 are the times at which the counts were commenced.

TABLE 7.1

Time (min)	Counts/ 20 sec	Counts/ min	Counts/min corrected for resolving time	Counts/min corrected for background	Log$_{10}$ (corrected count rate)
0	5,441	16,323	18,318	18,198	4·2600
$\frac{1}{2}$	4,150	12,450	13,578	13,458	4·1289
1	3,353	10,059	10,782	10,662	4·0278
$1\frac{1}{2}$	2,549	7,647	8,058	7,938	3·8997
2	2,065	6,195	6,463	6,343	3·8023
$2\frac{1}{2}$	1,478	4,434	4,569	4,449	3·6483
3	1,140	3,420	3,500	3,380	3·5289
$3\frac{1}{2}$	858	2,574	2,619	2,499	3·3977
4	641	1,923	1,947	1,827	3·2617
$4\frac{1}{2}$	521	1,563	1,579	1,459	3·1641
5	326	978	984	864	2·9365
$5\frac{1}{2}$	256	768	772	652	2·8142
6	209	627	630	510	2·7076
$6\frac{1}{2}$	173	519	521	401	2·6031
7	138	414	415	295	2·4698
$7\frac{1}{2}$	108	324	325	205	2·3118
8	80	240	240	120	2·0792
$8\frac{1}{2}$	69	207	207	87	1·9395

E

The sample was counted for 3 min about 20 min after the commencement of the experiment; 359 counts were obtained. The background count used to apply the correction in the table was therefore taken as 120 counts/min.

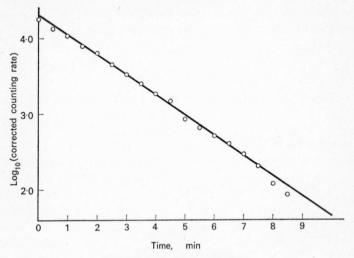

FIG. 7.2. The half-life of ^{234m}Pa.

A graph of $\log_{10}$ (corrected count rate) against time is shown in Fig. 7.2. The slope of this graph is $-0\cdot26$ min^{-1}. Using eqn. (5.1):

$$t_{\frac{1}{2}} = -\frac{0\cdot3008}{\text{gradient}} = -\frac{0\cdot3008}{0\cdot26} = 1\cdot16 \text{ min.}$$

Growth of ^{234}Pa

The experiment may now be repeated, but the aqueous layer is counted instead of the organic layer. It will be found that the counting rate increases with time as the ^{234}Th in the aqueous layer decays to ^{234m}Pa. The ^{234}Th beta particles cannot pass through the walls of an MX124/01 tube, since they have a low energy, but those from ^{234m}Pa can do so and are counted. As before each counting period can be 20 sec with 10 sec intervals for recording the number of counts obtained. About 20 min after the separation of the layers, the aqueous layer should be counted for 3 min in order to find the mean final counting rate.

The results should be treated by one of the methods discussed in Chapter 5 for obtaining the half-life of a material from its growth curve. It is not to be expected that the half-life obtained by this method will be as accurate as that obtained from counting the organic layer.

Suggestions for Further Work

If a solution of 1 g of uranyl nitrate in 10 ml of water is made and counted in a liquid sample tube, the efficiency of the tube for the detection of ^{234m}Pa beta particles may be estimated.

The percentage of ^{234m}Pa extracted by the organic liquid may be estimated in the following way. A solution containing a known weight, say 1 g of uranyl nitrate in 10 ml of 8 N hydrochloric acid, is shaken with 10 ml of the organic solvent and a stopwatch is started at the moment the two liquids become clearly separated. The organic layer is counted as soon as possible and the graph of $\log_{10}$ (corrected count rate) against time is extrapolated back to zero time. The efficiency of the extraction is approximately equal to the estimated counting rate at zero time divided by the counting rate of the same quantity of uranyl nitrate dissolved in 10 ml of water. The result is only approximate, since the beta particles will penetrate the organic solvent to reach the sensitive volume of the Geiger tube rather more easily than they will penetrate through the water.

The variation of the extraction efficiency with pH may be found. In addition the extraction efficiency obtained with various solvents may be compared. In such experiments it is desirable to let the organic layer decay to its minimum activity in order to ascertain whether any appreciable amount of ^{234}Th has also been extracted.

If it is desired to follow the change in counting rate of the two layers over a considerable period of time due to the ^{234}Th growth and decay, a solid sample should be prepared from each layer. This may be done by evaporating each layer in a crucible and igniting the nitrate to the oxide. The materials are mounted in a planchet using a trace of perspex dissolved in chloroform. The samples are counted with an absorber of about 35 mg/cm^2 so that only the beta particles from ^{234m}Pa are detected. The sample prepared from the organic layer has a very low initial counting rate, but its activity increases over a period of about 6 months. The sample prepared from the aqueous layer falls in activity over a similar period.

Experiment 7.9. The Separation of ^{234m}Pa by Precipitation with Zirconium Phosphate

In this experiment a little thorium is added as a hold-back carrier to prevent the precipitation of ^{234}Th with the ^{234m}Pa.

Prepare a solution of approximately 4 N hydrochloric acid using a safety pipette (about 1 part of concentrated hydrochloric acid to 2 parts of water). Dissolve 300 mg of uranyl nitrate, 15 mg of thorium nitrate and 30 mg of either of the acid sodium phosphates in 10 ml of the acid. Prepare a solution containing 40 mg of zirconium nitrate in 5 ml of dilute hydrochloric acid.

Heat the solution containing the uranium, thorium and the phosphate to boiling point and add a few drops of the zirconium nitrate solution. A very small amount of a precipitate of zirconium phosphate is formed. Quickly filter off this precipitate using the apparatus shown in Fig. 5.2 or 5.3 and twice wash it with a few millilitres of hot dilute hydrochloric acid. Immediately transfer the filter paper to a planchet and count under an end window Geiger tube. As in experiment 7.8, count for periods of 20 sec with intervals of 10 sec for recording the number of counts. The filtrate may be used for further ^{234m}Pa separations after an interval of 10 min.

Plot the decay curve of ^{234m}Pa and determine its half-life. In a typical experiment of this type, the counting rate falls from about 3000 counts/min to less than 100 counts/min when the sample is placed about 1 cm from the window of an MX123 tube.

Further Work

If the counting geometry is the same as in experiment 7.6, use the data from this experiment to estimate the fraction of the ^{234m}Pa precipitated with the zirconium phosphate.

It is very instructive to repeat the experiment without the use of thorium hold-back carrier. The counting rate will then only fall slightly, since the ^{234}Th precipitated with the ^{234m}Pa will continually re-generate the latter material.

Experiment 7.10. The Preparation of ^{234m}Pa and ^{234}Th by the Use of an Ion Exchange Column

Place a small plug of glass wool at the bottom of a 25 ml burette and make a 10 cm column of Amberlite IR-120 ion exchange resin by pouring a mixture of the resin and water into the burette. Wash the resin by passing a slow stream of water through it followed by about 150 ml of dilute hydrochloric acid. Finally wash with water.

Pass a solution of 10 g of uranyl nitrate in 50 ml of water through the column at a few drops per second. The ^{234}Th, the ^{234m}Pa and most of the uranium remain in the column. Pass about 100 ml of 2 N hydrochloric acid through the resin to remove the uranium and then wash with about 100 ml of water. The column is left for at least 10 min for ^{234m}Pa to be generated from the ^{234}Th.

^{234m}Pa Extraction

Allow the level of the liquid in the column to fall until it is just above the top of the resin. Pass 15 ml of 2 N hydrochloric acid through the column and place the effluent in a liquid sample Geiger tube. It may be counted as in experiments 7.8 and 7.9 and the half-life of ^{234m}Pa determined.

After about 10 min a further quantity of ^{234m}Pa may be extracted by passing a further 15 ml of hydrochloric acid through the column. The activity which is extracted will fall as the ^{234}Th decays with its half-life of 24·1 days. Thus it is necessary to regenerate the column about every 2 or 3 months by passing a further quantity of uranyl nitrate through it. Such a column is often referred to as a "UX$_2$ Cow", since UX$_2$ can be "milked" off it at intervals.

^{234}Th Extraction

The ^{234}Th in the column may be extracted by passing about 20 ml of a 0·5 N solution of oxalic acid through it. The acid may, if necessary, be destroyed by boiling the liquid with 2 ml of concentrated nitric acid and a few drops of hydrogen peroxide. The ^{234}Th solution may then be evaporated to a small volume, transferred to a planchet and evaporated to dryness. Its decay can be followed during the course of a month or more.

Experiment 7.11. The Preparation of ^{234}Th by Precipitation

0·25 g of uranyl nitrate is dissolved in 10 ml of water in a boiling tube. 1 ml of a solution containing 5 mg of ferric chloride per ml is added followed by an excess of ammonium carbonate solution. The mixture is shaken and heated so that the precipitate of ferric hydroxide coagulates. It is then filtered and washed with dilute ammonium carbonate solution. The residue is dissolved in a little dilute nitric acid and the ferric hydroxide reprecipitated by the addition of excess ammonium carbonate. It is filtered and washed, first with ammonium carbonate and finally with a little water. The material is transferred to a planchet and dried under an infrared lamp.

The material is counted from time to time over a period of not less than 4 weeks. Ideally the counting rate at each measurement should be compared with that of a long-lived counting source (such as that prepared in experiment 7.1) in order to make a correction for any change in the counting efficiency of the equipment. A decay curve may be plotted and the half-life of ^{234}Th found.

Growth of ^{234}Th

The filtrate from the first precipitation may be used to plot the growth curve of ^{234}Th. A small amount of ferric chloride solution is first added and the mixture is heated and filtered. Excess carbonate is removed by adding nitric acid until effervescence ceases. The liquid is then boiled to expel carbon dioxide. Very dilute ammonium hydroxide is added drop by drop (with stirring) until all of the uranium has been precipitated as ammonium diuranate. This material is filtered off, washed with methanol, dried and ignited to uranium oxide. It is mounted in a sample tray and counted at intervals of a few days over a period of at least a month. An aluminium absorber of about 35 mg/cm^2 is used to prevent alpha particles or weak beta particles from being counted.

The counting rate grows from a very small value with the half-life of ^{234}Th. This half-life may be estimated from the growth curve by one of the methods discussed in Chapter 5. It is instructive to plot growth and decay curves on the same graph and to compare the total activity with that of the untreated uranium salt initially used.

Further Comments

A similar experiment carried out by Crookes in 1900 (without the deliberate addition of any ferric hydroxide) is of considerable historical importance, since it led to the idea of growth and decay and the transmutation of elements undergoing radioactive change.

If it is desired to produce a solution of ^{234}Th almost free from iron, the re-precipitated ferric hydroxide may be dissolved in a little 6 N hydrochloric acid and placed in a separating funnel with 5 ml of ether. After shaking, the upper ether layer is discarded and the aqueous layer is successively shaken with a further two 5 ml portions of ether. The ferric chloride is removed by the ether leaving the ^{234}Th. If the solution is evaporated to dryness, only a small residue remains. This is an example of the use of a non-isotopic carrier to prepare a carrier free material.

Experiment 7.12. The Half-life of Thoron using an Ionisation Chamber

Two methods for estimating the half-life of thoron have been discussed in Chapter 6; this method is more suitable for an individual student. The ionisation chamber/dosimeter system used is that shown in Fig. 2.12 (p. 41). The method enables a half-life to be determined without any chemical separation, but the calculation is not so simple as in experiments where the activity is determined by counting.

The dosimeter is connected to the ionisation chamber and charged so that the indicator moves somewhat past the zero mark. The ionisation chamber is raised off the base and a little thoron is blown in from a thoron generator. (If the normal type of thoron generator consisting of thorium hydroxide contained in a plastic bottle is not available, a bottle of commercial thorium hydroxide may be opened and the mouth of the bottle placed in the chamber for a moment.) It may be necessary to experiment a few times to get a suitable amount of thoron into the ionisation chamber.

The stop-watch is started as the dosimeter indicator moves past the zero mark and the reading of the dosimeter is noted at suitable intervals until the indicator moves off the scale or until it almost comes to rest.

A graph of the dosimeter reading against time is plotted and is of the form shown in Fig. 7.3. The readings have no absolute but only a relative significance.

Let the dosimeter reading at any time t be d. Let the final reading after all the thoron has decayed be d_0. d is proportional to the total charge which has flowed, i.e. to the number of atoms

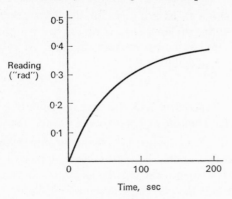

Fig. 7.3. The half-life of thoron.

which have decayed. Thus $(d_0 - d)/d_0$ is the fraction of the atoms which have yet to decay and is equal to N/N_0. But

$$\frac{N}{N_0} = e^{-\lambda t} \quad [\text{eqn. (1.3)}]$$

$$\frac{d_0 - d}{d_0} = \left(1 - \frac{d}{d_0}\right) = e^{-\lambda t}.$$

Hence $$d = d_0 (1 - e^{-\lambda t}).$$

This equation is of the same form as eqn. (3.3) for the growth of a nuclide from its long-lived parent. The half-life may be found by the methods discussed in Chapter 5 for finding half-lives from growth curves.

For example, values of dd/dt may be obtained from the graph of Fig. 7.3 and $\log_{10}(dd/dt)$ plotted against time. The slope of this graph is $-\lambda/2 \cdot 303$. Alternatively, the final reading d_0 may be found from the equation

$$d_0 = \frac{d_1^2}{2d_1 - d_2},$$

where d_1 is the reading after a time t and d_2 is the reading after a time $2t$. The value of the half-life is, of course, equal to the time taken for the reading to become equal to $d_0/2$.

E*

In this experiment, as in others for the determination of the half-life of thoron, the ionisation is produced by alpha particles from thoron and its decay product, thorium A, other contributions being negligible.

Experiment 7.13. The Determination
of the Half-life of Thoron using a G.M. Tube

A method has been devised by one manufacturer for counting the alpha particles emitted by thoron gas by employing a Geiger counter.[26] This experiment has the advantage over experiment 7.12 that the half-life can be determined by plotting a normal decay curve on semilogarithmic paper, but the maximum counting rate is usually less than that in many of the other half-life experiments described. Therefore one should not necessarily expect that the result will be highly accurate.

The apparatus used is supplied together with other apparatus as a kit by Panax Equipment Ltd.; it is shown in Fig. 7.4. An end-window Geiger tube such as the MX168 is employed, but somewhat higher counting rates can be obtained with a tube having a thinner window of larger area, for example the MX123 or EW3H tubes. The window of the Geiger tube is placed near to the window of a small plastic enclosure which will contain the gas. The window of this enclosure consists of a piece of extremely thin plastic material (about $0.9 \, \text{mg/cm}^2$ in thickness). The window is held in place by a rubber band. The alpha particles

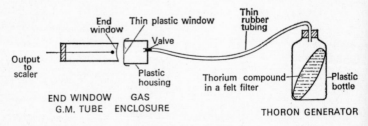

Fig. 7.4. The use of a G.M. tube for the determination of the half-life of thoron.

emitted from the thoron atoms in the enclosure have an energy which is just sufficient to enable them to pass through the window of the enclosure, through the small air gap and through the window of an MX168 Geiger tube. The air gap must be kept small.

At the start of the experiment the thoron generator is moved as far from the Geiger tube as the length of the rubber tubing will permit (about 1 ft). The background count is taken. Without appreciably altering the position of the thoron generator, it is pressed by hand so as to force the gas in it through the rubber tubing and through the valve into the gas enclosure. The air in the enclosure escapes from the junction of the window with the plastic housing. When the pressure on the thoron generator ceases, the valve prevents the gas from being sucked back along the rubber tubing.

Immediately after the gas had been placed in the chamber, the stop-watch and scaler are started simultaneously. The counting periods may be 20 sec with intermediate 10 sec intervals for the recording of the counts obtained. The stop-watch is left running during the whole of the experiment which is of about 5 min duration. After that the count rate remains almost constant.

A graph of $\log_{10}$ (corrected count rate) against time is plotted and the half-life of thoron is found from the slope of the graph in the usual way. Counting rates are usually fairly low and the correction for the finite resolving time is therefore small, but the background correction is important.

Both the alpha particles from thoron and those from thorium-A are counted, but the activity due to the longer-lived products lower in the thorium series is negligible.

Experiment 7.14. Measurement of Gas Flow Rate using Thoron Decay

In this experiment a stream of air or other gas is passed through a flask containing about 200 g of thorium hydroxide. After passing through a small glass-wool filter which removes any solid particles, the gas (containing thoron) passes into a long glass tube. A thin bare copper wire (about 32 s.w.g.) is held taut along the centre of the tube as shown in Fig. 7.5, passing through rubber bungs at each end of the tube. A length of aluminium foil also passes along the length of the tube, resting on its lower inside surface. A potential of 200 V or more is applied via a safety resistor between the central wire and the aluminium foil, the latter being made positive. The gas flow rate is adjusted so that it takes the gas about 3 min to pass through the tube.

After about 24 hr the wire is removed and cut into equal lengths. The most suitable length depends somewhat on the length of the tube, but lengths of 6 in. usually give reasonable results without

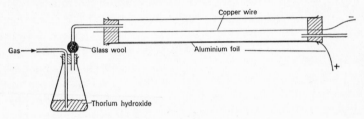

Fig. 7.5. Thoron gas flow apparatus.

entailing too many measurements. (These lengths should be marked on the wire before the commencement of the experiment in order to minimise handling of the wire when it has been made active.) Each length of copper wire should be dissolved in a minimum of nitric acid containing about 10 mg of lead nitrate and 10 mg of bismuth nitrate as carriers. Each solution should be diluted to about 10 times its volume, hydrogen sulphide passed to precipitate the lead, bismuth and copper and the mixtures filtered. Each precipitate should be mounted in a planchet, dried and counted. Any appreciable difference in the time of counting each sample should be corrected by allowing for the decay of the ^{212}Pb ($10 \cdot 6$ hr half-life) in equilibrium with the ^{212}Bi.

Plot a graph of $\log_{10}$ (counts per minute) against the distance of the wire section from the input end of the tube. From the slope of the graph and the half life of thoron (55 sec), deduce the linear rate of gas flow in the tube. Hence deduce the volume flow rate.

Experiment 7.15. The Preparation of ^{212}Pb from Thorium Hydroxide by Electrostatic Deposition

The apparatus is set up as shown in Fig. 7.6. A resistor is included in the circuit so that if the wires should touch inside the tube the current will be limited to about 100 μA. The voltage applied is not at all critical, any value between 100 V and 1000 V being suitable.

The apparatus should be left for some hours or, if possible,

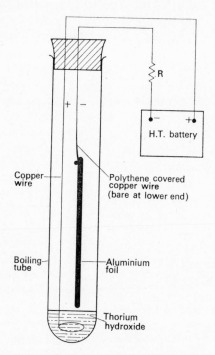

FIG. 7.6. Apparatus for electrodeposition of ThB.

for a day or more. Thoron gas is evolved from the thorium hydroxide and, after it has decayed to thorium A, the thorium B (^{212}Pb) is collected on the aluminium foil. This decays with a $10 \cdot 6$ hr half-life and hence reaches equilibrium activity on the foil in a few days. This method of collection not only provides "carrier free" isotopes, but it consumes none of the starting material. In addition all of the daughter products are so short-lived that the hazard they present is negligible. In some experimental manuals a more complicated apparatus is employed to obtain the active deposit. It has been found, however, that the apparatus shown in Fig. 7.6 will provide ample activity for educational work. A row of the boiling tubes may be permanently kept in a rack connected to a common battery in order to ensure that an ample supply of the active foil is available at any time without further preparation. Separate resistors may be used for each boiling tube so that if the wires touch in one tube the other tubes will still receive the applied voltage. The current consumption is quite negligible and the equipment need not be attended to more frequently than once per year.

The aluminium foil is removed with forceps. It should show an activity of perhaps 30,000 counts/min when brought near to an end-window Geiger tube. The foil should be placed in a small test-tube containing about 3 ml of $0 \cdot 5$ N nitric acid in which about 20 mg of lead nitrate have been dissolved. Almost all of the ^{212}Pb dissolves when the acid is warmed, the added lead acting as a carrier. About 20 mg of bismuth nitrate dissolved in a little dilute nitric acid should be added as a hold-back carrier for the ^{212}Bi formed during the decay of ^{212}Pb.

The lead (including ^{212}Pb) may be precipitated as lead sulphate by the addition of dilute sulphuric acid. A little alcohol should be added. Alternatively the lead may be precipitated as lead chromate by the addition of potassium chromate solution. The mixture is filtered and washed and the precipitate transferred to a planchet for counting. It should be counted for a period of about 2 min each quarter of an hour for the first few hours, after which it may be counted about 2 or 3 times per day for 5 days (if convenient). The initial counting rate may be of the order of 20,000 counts/min.

A graph of $\log_{10}$ (counting rate) against time rises to a maximum during the first few hours, since initially ^{212}Pb alone is present, but the amount of ^{212}Bi formed by the decay of ^{212}Pb gradually reaches its equilibrium activity. After passing through a maximum, the graph becomes linear. The half-life of ^{212}Pb may be found from the slope of the linear part of the graph in the usual way.

The beta radiation from the ^{212}Pb (maximum energies $0 \cdot 57$ and $0 \cdot 33$ MeV) is much less energetic than that from the ^{212}Bi (maximum energy $2 \cdot 25$ MeV). When the ^{212}Bi has reached an equilibrium activity, an absorption curve may be plotted. This curve clearly shows two linear portions for the ^{212}Pb and ^{212}Bi beta energies (as in Fig. 2.8) (p. 35). It is not possible to separate the two beta energies of the ^{212}Pb in this apparatus. The half-thickness for each type of radiation may be estimated. The net count due to the ^{212}Bi may be found by extrapolating the part of the curve obtained with thick absorbers back to zero absorber thickness. The net count due to the ^{212}Pb may be found by subtraction of the count due to ^{212}Bi from the total count. The ^{208}Tl contributes to the ^{212}Bi count.

During the first few hours it is instructive to measure the effect of an absorber of about 100 mg/cm^2 on the counting rate. It will be found that such an absorber will initially reduce the counting rate by a factor of over 10, but after a few hours it will reduce it by a smaller factor. This shows that the relative proportion of the radionuclides is changing with time.

Specimen Results

A graph of the decay of ^{212}Pb is shown in Fig. 7.7. The measurements were taken over five successive days, the gaps between each set of points on the graph being due to the fact that it was not convenient to take readings during the night. Zero time was taken as the time of the first reading which was sometime after the time of separation of the ^{212}Pb. If zero time had been taken as the

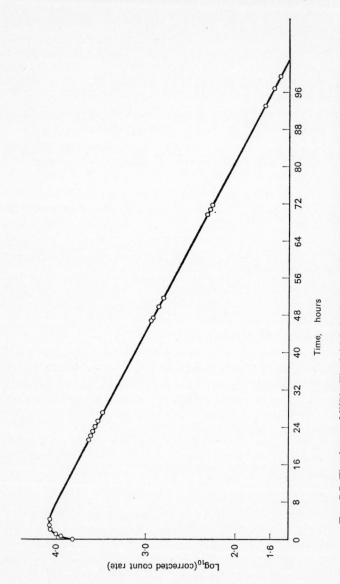

FIG. 7.7. The decay of ²¹²Pb. The initial rise is due to the growth of the daughter product ²¹²Bi.

time of separation of the ^{212}Pb, the graph could have been extrapolated back in order to estimate the counting rate at this moment of separation. The increase of the counting rate at the beginning of the experiment due to the growth of ^{212}Bi is clearly shown.

The slope of the straight-line portion of the graph was found to be $-0 \cdot 0275$ hr $^{-1}$. Using eqn. (5.1), the half-life is found to be $10 \cdot 9$ hr. This is in reasonable agreement with the values quoted in the literature, namely about $10 \cdot 64$ hr.

An absorption curve for the ^{212}Pb–^{212}Bi equilibrium mixture is shown in Fig. 7.8. The counting rates due to the two isotopes

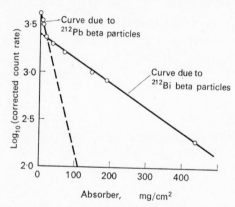

FIG. 7.8. An absorption curve for a ^{212}Pb–^{212}Bi mixture showing the two main energy components.

are not equal, since the counting efficiency for the beta particles from the ^{212}Bi is somewhat greater than for those from the ^{212}Pb owing to their higher energy.

Experiment 7.16. The Preparation of ^{212}Bi by Electrostatic Deposition

In this experiment a solution of ^{212}Pb and its decay products should be prepared from an active aluminium foil obtained as in experiment 7.15. After the lead has been precipitated ^{212}Bi may be precipitated from the filtrate by passing hydrogen sulphide through the liquid. The mixture is filtered and washed with water.

The precipitate is transferred to a planchet and counted under an end-window Geiger tube for periods of about 2 min each quarter of an hour for as long as possible (or until the activity remaining is small). An initial counting rate of about 20,000 counts/min can be obtained in this way and the decay can be followed over a period of about 8 hr if desired, since the half-life of the material is about an hour. A graph of $\log_{10}$ (counting rate) against time is plotted and the half-life of the ^{212}Bi determined.

In between the measurements which are made to determine the half-life, counts may be made with absorbers of various thicknesses in order to estimate the energy of the beta particles being emitted. The absorber measurements must be corrected for decay which has occurred, e.g. by finding the counting rate which would have been obtained with each absorber at zero time. The logarithm of the corrected counting rate may be plotted against the absorber thickness and the beta energy estimated from the half-thickness. In interpreting the results, the presence of the decay product ^{208}Tl should not be forgotten.

Alternative Methods

If the ^{212}Pb precipitate is not required or if it is desired to avoid the use of hydrogen sulphide, the ^{212}Bi together with carrier bismuth may be deposited on a nickel disc, the lead remaining in solution.

The active material is dissolved from the aluminium foil as in experiment 7.15 by a little hot $0 \cdot 5$ N nitric acid. About 20 mg of lead nitrate and 30 mg of bismuth nitrate are added as carriers. A piece of nickel about $\frac{1}{2}$ in. in diameter, previously cleaned from grease with nitric acid and waxed on one side, is placed in the solution which is then warmed. Bismuth is formed as a black deposit on the unwaxed side of the nickel disc which may be transferred to a planchet after about 10 min.

The remainder of the experiment is performed in the way which has already been described.

^{212}Bi may also be obtained from a solution prepared from an active aluminium foil by the following method. After the addition of lead and bismuth carrier solutions, excess sodium hydroxide is added to precipitate the bismuth. Provided that an excess of the precipitant is employed, the lead will remain in solution as sodium plumbite. The precipitate containing the bismuth is filtered off and counted.

Experiment 7.17. The Preparation of ^{212}Pb and ^{212}Bi by Solvent Extraction[27]

Dissolve 1 g of thorium nitrate in 10 ml of water and add dilute ammonium hydroxide drop by drop with shaking until the pH rises to about $3 \cdot 0$ (test with pH paper). Any thorium hydroxide precipitated should now re-dissolve on vigorous shaking. Add about 5 ml of a 1% solution of sodium diethyl dithiocarbamate (which acts as a complexing agent) and 20 ml of ether. Shake in a separating funnel, separate the ether layer and evaporate it to dryness. Extract the residue with a few millilitres of hot dilute nitric acid, adding 20 mg each of lead nitrate and bismuth nitrate as carriers.

The lead (including the ^{212}Pb) may be precipitated with sulphuric acid as in experiment 7.15, whilst the bismuth may be obtained by precipitation with hydrogen sulphide.

Experiment 7.18. Backscatter

Prepare a solution of ^{212}Pb from an active aluminium foil as in experiment 7.15 and evaporate it nearly to dryness. Place a few drops of the solution on a thin piece of plastic and allow it to evaporate in a warm room. Leave it for at least 4 hr so that the ^{212}Bi will reach equilibrium.

Place the active plastic under an end-window Geiger tube so that there is nothing immediately underneath it. Count the source.

Then repeat the counting with aluminium absorbers of various thicknesses beneath the source. Note that the counting rate increases with increasing absorber thickness until a maximum value is reached. Lead absorbers should also be used to ascertain whether the amount of backscattering is greater or less than when aluminium absorbers are employed. Correct for any decay of the source between the various counts.

Estimate the error caused by backscattering when a ^{212}Pb–^{212}Bi source is counted on a normal aluminium planchet using the geometry of your equipment.

Experiment 7.19. The Preparation of ^{208}Tl by Liquid Extraction

An active aluminium foil is prepared as in experiment 7.15. The active deposit is dissolved from the foil by boiling it for a few minutes with a few millilitres of $0·5$ N nitric acid in a small test tube, 20 mg each of lead nitrate, bismuth nitrate and thallous nitrate being added as carriers. The solution is evaporated to a small volume and 10 ml of 6 N hydrochloric acid (equal parts of the concentrated acid and water) are added followed by about $0·5$ ml of 20 volume hydrogen peroxide. The solution is boiled for a few minutes to oxidise thallous ions to the thallic state. After it has been cooled, it is poured into separating funnel and 10 ml of iso-butylmethyl ketone are added.

A second separating funnel is now prepared. It contains 10 ml of concentrated hydrochloric acid together with 20 mg each of lead nitrate and bismuth nitrate dissolved in a small volume of water.

The first separating funnel is shaken for about half a minute and the lower layer containing the ^{212}Pb and the ^{212}Bi is discarded. The thallic chloride is present in the upper organic layer which is poured into the second separating funnel. The mixture is shaken, the lower acid layer again discarded and the upper layer is run into a liquid sample Geiger tube. The counting should be carried out for periods of 30 sec with 15 sec intervals between the counting periods for recording the number of counts obtained. A decay curve is plotted and the half-life of thallium-208 is determined.

Further Comments

It is interesting to repeat this experiment carrying out only the first separation, the washing being omitted. In this case it will be found that the activity remaining after the ^{208}Tl has decayed will be quite appreciable, since some ^{212}Pb and ^{212}Bi tend to be extracted with the ^{208}Tl. Although the separation is not nearly so good as that of experiment 7.8, the longer half-life of ^{208}Tl results in a smaller amount of decay during the time taken by the washing operation.

The experiment may be carried out using about 10 ml of a 50% solution of thorium nitrate instead of the solution prepared from the active aluminium foil. The carriers are added as before and the thallous ions oxidised to the thallic state.

Experiment 7.20. The Preparation
of ^{208}Tl by Precipitation

The deposit from an active aluminium foil prepared as in experiment 7.15 is removed by boiling it with a few millilitres of $0 \cdot 5$ N nitric acid in a small test tube, but no lead or bismuth carriers are added. 20 mg each of ferric chloride and thallous nitrate dissolved in a little water are added followed by a little ammonium hydroxide. The mixture is boiled to coagulate the precipitate of ferric hydroxide. The ^{212}Pb and the ^{212}Bi are precipitated with the ferric hydroxide, since these elements are present only in carrier free concentrations, but the ^{208}Tl remains in solution. The liquid is quickly filtered under suction and the filtrate poured into a liquid sample tube. It is counted for periods of 30 sec with 15 sec intervals. The half-life is determined from a decay graph.

In a subsequent experiment the rise of ^{208}Tl activity in the precipitate may be measured.

F

It is interesting to repeat the experiment without the addition of any thallium carrier. Much of the ^{208}Tl is then precipitated along with the other decay products.

Experiment 7.21. The Separation of ^{208}Tl by Adsorption

Some heteropolyacid ammonium salts can adsorb certain monovalent cations in exchange for ammonium ions. For example, ammonium phosphomolybdate will adsorb rubidium, caesium and mercurous mercury ions. In this experiment the ^{208}Tl ions present in a solution of a thorium salt are selectively adsorbed onto ammonium phosphomolybdate, the other decay products remaining in solution. Only a very small quantity of ammonium phosphomolybdate is required.

Dissolve 7 g of thorium nitrate in 10 ml of dilute nitric acid. Add about 20 mg of finely powdered ammonium phosphomolybdate and shake for about 1 min. Filter through a 21 mm glass-fibre filter, quickly wash with about 10 ml of dilute nitric acid in four portions and transfer the glass-fibre filter to a planchet.

Count for periods of 30 sec with intervals of 15 sec for recording the number of counts obtained. The sample should be placed as close as possible to the Geiger tube window. Plot a decay curve and determine the half-life of ^{208}Tl.

Further Comments

An initial counting rate of the order of 5000 per min can be obtained in this experiment. If water is used instead of dilute nitric acid for washing the residue, other active materials will remain adsorbed on it and the counting rate will not fall to a low value when the ^{208}Tl has decayed.

The capability of ammonium phosphomolybdate for adsorbing ions is very dependent on its method of preparation. Ideally it should be prepared by a method described by Smit, Jacobs and Robb,[28] but it has been found that ammonium phosphomolybdate prepared by warming a solution of a sodium phosphate in nitric acid with excess ammonium molybdate is quite satis-factory for use in this experiment. The precipitate obtained should be washed several times with 1 N ammonium nitrate solution.

Experiment 7.22. The Use of ^{212}Pb as a Tracer

In this experiment ^{212}Pb obtained from thorium hydroxide by electro-deposition is used to measure the solubility of lead bromide in various solutions.

Dissolve 50 mg of lead nitrate and 50 mg of bismuth nitrate in 2 ml of $0 \cdot 5$ N nitric acid. Boil an active aluminium foil (obtained as in experiment 7.15) in the mixture for a few minutes. Evaporate the solution almost to dryness to remove most of the nitric acid. Dilute the solution to about 10 ml, dissolve $0 \cdot 7495$ g of lead nitrate in it and make the volume up to 20 ml. This solution (solution A) contains 25 mg of Pb^{++} per ml.

Dilute 2 ml of solution A to 10 ml. The resulting solution (solution B) will later be counted in a liquid sample tube. It contains 5 mg of Pb^{++} per ml.

Add excess dilute potassium bromide solution to the remaining 18 ml of solution A, filter off the precipitate of active lead bromide and wash it a few times with distilled water.

Slurry a small amount (about $0 \cdot 1$ g) of the lead bromide with 12 ml of distilled water and shake for 10 min. Note the temperature at the end of this operation and adjust it if necessary. Filter and label the filtrate "Solution C".

Allow the solutions to stand for a few hours (or overnight) so that the bismuth decay product comes into equilibrium with the lead isotope. Count solutions B and C separately in a liquid sample tube. From the known concentration of lead in solution B, calculate its concentration in solution C. Hence calculate the solubility and the solubility product of lead bromide. If the activities of these solutions are measured within a few minutes of each other, it will be unnecessary to allow for the decay of the ^{212}Pb, since it has a $10 \cdot 6$ hr half-life. After standing overnight counting rates of about 500 per min are easily obtained using an MX124/01 liquid sample tube.

Further Work

It is instructive to investigate the solubility of lead bromide in solutions of sodium bromide and of lead nitrate of varying concentrations. Concentrated solutions should be avoided, however, since a change of density of the solution will affect the counting rate somewhat. Solutions are made by slurrying about $0 \cdot 1$ g of active lead bromide with 12 ml of a solution containing sodium bromide or lead nitrate of known concentration. After filtration, the solution is allowed to stand for some hours before being counted with solution B.

A similar experiment may be carried out with lead chloride, but owing to its greater solubility $2 \cdot 3485$ g of lead nitrate should be added instead of $0 \cdot 7495$ g. The solution corresponding to solution B will then contain 15 mg of Pb^{++} per ml. In the case of lead iodide, the solubility is lower and the 50 mg of lead nitrate initially added as a carrier will probably be adequate. The addition of too much lead nitrate will result in the activity of the solutions being too low, whereas the addition of too little lead nitrate will result in the amount of lead bromide, chloride or iodide formed being insufficient for the experiment.

Experiment 7.23. The Determination of the Surface Area of a Precipitate[27]

In this experiment the surface area of a precipitate of lead sulphate is determined by the use of ^{212}Pb. The lead on the surface of the precipitate is allowed to exchange with the lead in the solution and the measured ratio (^{212}Pb in solution)/(^{212}Pb on surface) is assumed to be the same as the ratio (lead in solution)/(lead on surface). The amount of lead in solution is found from the known solubility of lead sulphate. Thus a value for the amount of lead on the surface is found and, if a value for the surface area occupied by one molecule of lead sulphate is assumed, the surface area of the precipitate is obtained.

It is important to leave the precipitate in contact with the active solution for a time which allows the exchange to occur to a reasonable degree of completion. On the other hand, if the exchange is allowed to proceed for an excessive time, some of the atoms beneath the surface layer may exchange with those in the solution.

Procedure

It is first necessary to prepare a saturated solution of lead sulphate containing some ^{212}Pb activity. Prepare some inactive lead sulphate by mixing a solution containing a few grammes of lead nitrate with some dilute sulphuric acid. Filter and wash the residue several times with a fairly large volume of water. Do not allow the precipitate to dry, as this may result in an alteration of the surface area. Shake the lead sulphate with 25 ml of distilled water. It is best to use an automatic shaker or stirrer, but if intermittent shaking by hand is carried out, it should be continued for a few days. The temperature should be kept at about normal room temperature. Decant the solution leaving a very small amount of the solid lead sulphate in the liquid. This liquid should be added to a solution containing ^{212}Pb which has been obtained as in experiment 7.15, most of the nitric acid having been removed by evaporation. Shake for about $\frac{1}{2}$–1 hr and filter. The filtrate (solution A) is a saturated solution of lead sulphate containing ^{212}Pb.

Add 15 ml of solution A to about a gramme of moist inactive lead sulphate. Shake for a quarter of an hour keeping the temperature constant. Filter through a weighed sintered-glass crucible, keeping the filtrate separate from the washings. Heat the crucible in an oven and weigh. Allow the filtrate to stand for some hours (or overnight) so that the ^{212}Pb and ^{212}Bi come into equilibrium. Count it in a liquid sample tube. If solution A is counted at about the same time, the decay correction will be negligible.

Calculate the amount of ^{212}Pb remaining in the solution as a fraction of that which is absorbed on the precipitate. From the solubility of lead sulphate (0·0042 g per 100 ml of water at 20°C) estimate the weight of lead sulphate at the surface using the relationship

$$\frac{\text{Amount of } ^{212}\text{Pb on surface}}{\text{Amount of } ^{212}\text{Pb remaining in solution}}$$
$$= \frac{\text{Weight of lead in surface layer of the solid}}{\text{Weight of lead in solution}}$$

Hence if the area occupied by one molecule of lead sulphate is 2×10^{-15} cm², estimate the surface area of a gramme of the lead sulphate.

Experiment 7.24. The Determination of Small Concentrations of Uranium or Thorium by means of Nuclear Emulsions

Very small concentrations of uranium or thorium (less than 1 μg/l) can be detected in aqueous solution by the use of a nuclear emulsion if the material is allowed to remain in the emulsion for some time before development.

Make a solution containing 0·1 g UO$_2^{++}$ or Th^{++++} per 100 ml of water. Using the recommended dark-room illumination, soak a nuclear plate (e.g. an Ilford 3 in. by 1 in. plate of emulsion thickness 50 μ) in this solution for 15 min. Simultaneously place another plate in the unknown solution for the same time. Dry the plates with a filter paper and leave them in a dark box for a week. Develop the plates together according to the manufacturer's recommendations, wash and fix. The fixing time may be greater than that required for normal photographic negatives; the fixing solution should be agitated periodically. Wash the plates under running water for at least an hour and allow them to dry.

Examine the plates under a high-power microscope using a $\frac{1}{6}$ in. or a $\frac{1}{12}$ in. objective. Find the ratio of the mean number of tracks visible in the field of view of the microscope in each case and calculate the concentration of the unknown solution using the known concentration of the other solution.

It is instructive to use several solutions of known concentration and to vary the time between the introduction of the uranium or thorium and the development.

Experiment 7.25. Estimation of the Branching Ratio of ThC using a Nuclear Emulsion

The isotope ThC (^{212}Bi) decays partly into a short-lived alpha emitter ThC' (^{212}Po) and partly into ThC'' (^{208}Tl) which is a beta emitter. The short-lived alpha emitter ThC' provides long alpha tracks, since the alpha particles from this material have the exceptionally high energy of 8·78 MeV. The proportion of five-pronged "stars" containing these long tracks is found.

Using the recommended dark-room illumination, soak a nuclear plate in a 0·05% solution of thorium sulphate for 15 min. Dry the plate with a filter paper and leave it in a dark box for at least a week. Develop the plate after this time and fix. Wash and allow it to dry.

Using a $\frac{1}{6}$ in. or $\frac{1}{12}$ in. objective, examine the plate under a microscope. Count the total number of stars having five tracks visible in the field of view of the microscope at various parts of the plate and the number of these which contain the long track due to ThC'. Hence state the percentage of the ThC which decays to ThC'. A reasonably large number of stars must be counted if a fairly accurate result is required.

Experiment 7.26. The Determination of Long Half-lives

No change in the activity of an isotope with a half-life exceeding a million years will be detectable in the course of any experiment. The half-lives of such elements must therefore be calculated from the activity of a known weight of the material. Nuclear emulsions are especially useful for the determination of the half-lives of

very long-lived alpha emitters, since the number of tracks formed
in the emulsion increases with time. A half-life of over 10^{18} years
(^{209}Bi) has been found by this method.

1. *An Approximate Method*

In this experiment a nuclear emulsion of known thickness is
soaked in a weak solution (about $0 \cdot 05\%$) of a uranium or a
thorium salt for about 15 min. It is left in a dark box for a week
before being processed. The number of stars in the case of thorium
or straight lines in the case of uranium in the field of view of a
high-power microscope are counted.

The area of the field of view of the microscope must be found.
This may be calculated from published data on the microscope
or alternatively it may be found directly by counting the number
of lines of a suitable diffraction grating of known line spacing
which are visible across the field of view.

The microscope measurements enable the number of disintegrations per cubic centimetre of the emulsion which occur in
one week to be found. The number of uranium or thorium atoms
per millilitre of the emulsion is assumed to be the same as the
number per millilitre of the solution. This assumption that the
emulsion absorbs its own volume of the solution undoubtedly
limits the accuracy of this experiment.

From the number of atoms per unit volume N and the number
of disintegrations per unit volume per second $-dN/dt$, the
radioactive constant λ for the decay may be found from the
normal decay equation

$$- dN/dt = \lambda N.$$

Hence the half-life may be found.

It is desirable to use uranium of natural isotopic composition
for this experiment, since the number of disintegrations of ^{238}U
in the emulsion volume is then approximately equal to the number
of tracks divided by two (an equal number of tracks are formed
by the decay of ^{234}U). If ordinary depleted uranium is used, the

exact isotopic composition should be obtained from the manufacturers of the specimen used.

In the case of thorium the number of disintegrations may be taken as equal to the total number of three-, four- and five-pronged stars provided that the radiothorium present in the sample is in equilibrium with the thorium.

2. *A More Accurate Method*

About 0·5 g of uranyl nitrate is dissolved in 100 ml of alcohol. 0·01 ml of this solution is measured in an micropipette and placed on the surface of a nuclear emulsion in the darkroom. It evaporates leaving the uranium salt partly in the emulsion and partly on the surface. Another nuclear plate is placed on the uranium-loaded plate (emulsion side to emulsion side). After a known time (a few days) the pair of plates are processed together.

The plates are examined under a high-power microscope and the number of tracks per unit area is measured in various places within the part of the emulsion containing the uranium. Some tracks will be formed in the lower plate and some in the upper plate. The average number of tracks per unit area in the two plates should therefore be doubled. Only tracks which exceed half the normal track length should be counted. The distribution of the track density within the area covered by the drop should be examined to ascertain if there is any non-uniform distribution of the tracks. If so, measurements of track density should be made at points which will give a reasonably accurate mean value of the track density. The area of the drop is equal to the area covered by the tracks.

The calculation is similar to that used for the approximate method. If time permits, a number of such experiments should be set up and the plates developed in pairs at intervals of a few days. It is also desirable to determine the track density in a blank plate. In the case of uranium, allowance should be made for the tracks due to the decay of ^{234}U.

Experiment 7.27. Alpha Particle Ranges
in a Nuclear Emulsion

The success of this experiment depends upon the availability of a really good microscope which will measure distances accurately in both the vertical and the horizontal directions.

Examine a nuclear plate containing alpha particle tracks from uranium under a high-power microscope using a $\frac{1}{12}$ in. oil-immersion objective and a $\times 10$ eyepiece. Choosing tracks which are as nearly horizontal as possible, measure the horizontal lengths of at least thirty tracks. In choosing horizontal tracks, take care not to select them according to their length. Measure also the vertical distance between the ends of each track. The apparent depth and the real depth may be taken as equal when an oil-immersion objective is being used, but the vertical distance must be multiplied by a factor of about $2 \cdot 5$ to allow for the vertical shrinkage of the emulsion when the silver bromide is removed during fixing. The total length of each track is then found using Pythagoras' theorem.

Identify the tracks due to ^{238}U ($4 \cdot 19$ MeV) and the rather longer ones due to ^{234}U (72% of $4 \cdot 77$ MeV and 28% of $4 \cdot 72$ MeV). Find the relative proportion of these two types of track. Is there any evidence for tracks of an intermediate length from ^{235}U atoms (83% of the atoms of this isotope emit $4 \cdot 40$ MeV alpha particles and 10% emit $4 \cdot 56$ MeV alpha particles)? The number of tracks from ^{235}U disintegrations will be only a few per cent of the total number of tracks, the exact percentage depending on whether depleted uranium or uranium of natural isotopic composition is used.

Using the same microscope, examine a plate which contains the tracks of the alpha particles from a thorium salt. Choosing tracks which are as nearly horizontal as possible, measure the length of the very long alpha tracks due to ThC′ ($8 \cdot 78$ MeV) and the length of the shortest tracks due to ^{232}Th (76% are of $4 \cdot 01$ MeV and 24% are of $3 \cdot 95$ MeV). Measure the length of some of the other tracks and try to identify the emitting isotopes from their alpha particle energies (Appendix 2). Any star containing five tracks is due to an atom of radiothorium which has decayed to thorium D (Fig. 3.2) (p. 44). Stars containing four tracks are due to the decay of radiothorium to thorium B or to the decay of thorium X to thorium D, whilst stars containing three tracks are due to thorium X decaying to thorium B. If an atom of ThX (half-life $3 \cdot 64$ days) decays, the product atom thoron (half-life 55 sec) and the following decay product thorium A (half-life $0 \cdot 16$ sec) are virtually certain to decay during the week or so before the plate is processed. The tracks due to the alpha particles from thorium will be single ones, since the probability that the product atom, Mesothorium 1 (half-life $6 \cdot 7$ years), will decay during a week or so is negligible.

Let R be the alpha particle range and E the particle energy in megaelectron volts. Using the mean values of R you have obtained plot a graph of $\log_{10} R$ against $\log_{10} E$. Check that R is proportional to E^x (where x is a constant) and estimate the value of x from your graph.

Experiment 7.28. The Estimation of the Half-life of ^{40}K

A weighed amount of uranium oxide is used to calculate the efficiency of an end-window Geiger counting system. A weighed amount of a potassium salt is then counted using the same equipment and the same geometry. Assuming a value for the relative abundance of potassium-40 in natural potassium, the half-life is estimated.

Weigh a 50 mm diameter planchet, first empty and then containing a thin evenly spread layer of uranium oxide, U_3O_8. Count using a range of absorbers from about 35 mg/cm² to 200 mg/cm². Plot a graph of $\log_{10}$ (counting rate) against the absorber thickness and extrapolate back to zero thickness. Estimate the thickness of the layer of uranium oxide in the planchet and correct the counting rate for self-absorption losses using the results obtained in experiment 7.6.

Calculate the number of beta particles given out per minute by the ^{234}Pa isotope which is in radioactive equilibrium with the

^{238}U. Hence find the counting efficiency of the system. (This value will not be the same as that obtained in experiment 7.6, since a large planchet is now being used.)

Place a fairly thick evenly spread layer of potassium chloride (or another non-deliquescent potassium salt) in the planchet and weigh. Count the sample for a fairly long time without the use of any absorber. The geometry should be exactly the same as in the previous part of the experiment. Determine the background rate as accurately as possible. If time permits, count samples of potassium salts of various thicknesses.

The maximum energy of the beta particles emitted by ^{40}K is 1·325 MeV. Find the half-thickness $d_{\frac{1}{2}}$ from the approximate relationship $d_{\frac{1}{2}} = 46\ E^{3/2}$ mg/cm^2 and the absorption coefficient μ from $\mu = 0·693/d_{\frac{1}{2}}$. Hence calculate the self-absorption correction from eqn. (2.3). Using the estimated efficiency of the counting system, find the number of disintegrations per minute per gramme of the sample. The abundance of ^{40}K in natural potassium is 0·0119%. Calculate the activity of 1 gramme of pure ^{40}K and hence estimate the radioactive constant for the beta decay of this isotope. 89% of ^{40}K undergoes beta decay, the remaining 11% undergoing electron capture with the emission of a gamma ray. Estimate the half-life of ^{40}K assuming that 89% of the disintegrations have given rise to detectable beta particles.

A number of approximations have been made in this experiment; whilst an accurate result should not therefore be expected, the error is usually less than 20%.

A similar experiment may be performed with a rubidium salt. Natural rubidium contains 27·85% of ^{87}Rb. This isotope, of half-life $4·8 \times 10^{10}$ years, emits beta particles which have the rather low maximum energy of 0·275 MeV. Although the specific activity of natural rubidium compounds is higher than that of similar natural potassium compounds (owing to the greater abundance of ^{87}Rb in natural rubidium than ^{40}K in natural potassium), the self-absorption correction for a layer of given thickness will be much greater owing to the low particle energy. All atoms of ^{87}Rb decay by negative beta emission.

Experiment 7.29. The Separation of ThX (^{224}Ra) with MsTh 1 (^{228}Ra)

30 mg each of lead nitrate and barium nitrate dissolved in a little water are added to 10 ml of a 2% solution of thorium nitrate. Carbonate free ammonium hydroxide is added until the precipitation is complete. The mixture is filtered, the filtrate being preserved for the second part of the experiment. Wash the precipitate with water, dissolve it in a minimum of dilute nitric acid and reprecipitate with ammonium hydroxide as before. Discard this filtrate. Wash the precipitate first with water and then with alcohol, dry it under an infrared lamp and count periodically for a few days. This material will be referred to as precipitate A.

The filtrate from the first precipitation is treated with dilute sulphuric acid, heated to the boiling point and the precipitated barium sulphate is filtered off. It is washed, first with water and then with alcohol, and dried under an infrared lamp. This precipitate, precipitate B, is counted periodically over a few days.

Precipitate A consists of the hydroxides of thorium, radiothorium, mesothorium 2 and lead-212. Lead nitrate carrier was added initially to ensure that the precipitation of the lead-212 would be virtually complete. Some ThX (^{224}Ra) and MsTh 1 (^{228}Ra) tend to be absorbed on the precipitate and therefore the precipitation must be repeated at least once. If the precipitate is counted with a thin absorber (about 10 mg/cm^2), the alpha particles from thorium and radiothorium will not be detected. The activity of the precipitate will fall as the lead-212 (half-life 10·6 hr) and the mesothorium 2 (half-life 6·13 hr) decay away, but will rise again as the beta emitters ThB, ThC and ThC″ are formed from radiothorium.

Mesothorium 1 and thorium X are two isotopes of radium; their chemical properties are therefore similar to those of barium. They remain in solution during the first precipitation but are precipitated along with the barium sulphate. ThX is an alpha emitter and is therefore not detected if a thin absorber is employed during the counting. Mesothorium 1 emits beta particles of a very low energy which cannot pass through the absorber. Thus the initial counting rate of precipitate B is very low, but it rises to a maximum as ThX decays to ThB and as MsTh 1 decays to MsTh 2. The activity subsequently falls due to the decay of ThX.

This experiment is similar to the famous one carried out by Rutherford and Soddy in 1902. They precipitated thorium hydroxide (without the addition of any carrier) with ammonium hydroxide and found that that precipitate was almost inactive. The filtrate was evaporated to dryness and heated to remove ammonium compounds. The small residue which remained had a measured activity equal to that of the thorium salt initially used.

An alternative way of partially separating ThX involves the addition of a fairly concentrated solution of sodium carbonate to a solution of thorium nitrate containing 20 mg of barium chloride as a carrier. Thorium carbonate is soluble in sodium carbonate solution and the latter is added until only a small amount of a precipitate of barium carbonate remains. It is transferred to a planchet and counted over a period of a few days using an absorber of about 10 mg/cm^2. The precipitate so obtained will contain ^{212}Pb and ^{212}Bi in addition to the required ThX and MsTh 1.

Experiment 7.30. The Concentration
of Airborne Radioisotopes

Ordinary air contains an activity of perhaps a micro-microcurie of radon per litre and about one-fiftieth of this amount of thoron, the concentration varying considerably with the place and time. These gases are evolved from the radium and thorium contained in the soil, etc. They cannot themselves easily be concentrated in order to obtain a sample with a measurable activity, but their decay products can be obtained in two main ways. In addition the air contains fission products which result from nuclear explosions.

Method 1

One method by which decay products of the inert gases can be obtained from the air involves the sucking of a large volume of air through a filter paper and the measurement of the resulting activity of this paper by means of a Geiger tube.[29] Most of the activity of the decay products is absorbed on particles of dust which are trapped by the filter paper. It has been estimated that only about 1% of the beta activity passes through a suitable paper. Some of the activity is probably attracted to the filter paper because it is attached to minute charged particles.

The amount of air drawn through the filter paper may be about 1000–10,000 l./hr. The paper will be rendered grey by particles of dust, but in a typical case will provide rather over 100 counts/min. The logarithm of the counting rate may be plotted against time and the half-lives of the nuclides present on the paper estimated. If the air is sucked through the paper for about an hour, the most prominent part of the decay curve will show a half-life of about half an hour (due to RaB), but a second component of half-life about 10 hr (ThB) will also be found. If air is sucked through the paper for 2 days, the activity of RaB reaches a saturation value and that due to ThB becomes much more prominent. In addition a long-lived activity becomes apparent; this is due to fission products from nuclear explosions. The air inside a building will often show a greater activity than the outside air owing to the radon and thoron emitted from the walls, but laboratories containing unsealed radium or thorium compounds show a far greater level of activity.

Method 2

The second method involves the natural concentration of the decay products of the emanations in rain water. Fresh rain-water obtained from the first shower which has occurred for some time will provide a count rate in an MX124/01 liquid sample tube of typically 10 counts/min above the background. After it has been raining for some time, the concentration of the active materials is much reduced both in the air and in the rain-water. The activity initially decays with a half-life of about half an hour.

The activity in the rain-water must be concentrated further if it is desired to follow the decay of the nuclides over a period of more than a few hours. Evaporation is slow and tedious compared with other methods. Even simple filtration of the water will result in an appreciable fraction of the activity remaining on the filter paper, since a large portion of it tends to be adsorbed on minute particles of dust and dirt. A rather better method involves the addition of about 50 mg of aluminium sulphate or ordinary alum to about 2 gal of fresh rain-water followed by the precipitation of the aluminium as its hydroxide with ammonia. The resulting precipitate contains about 80% of the activity of the water and may be counted under an end-window tube. In some cases the activity due to fission products may be counted in a sample for a very long time after the naturally occurring radioactive materials have decayed away. Approximate estimates of the activity of the original rain-water may be made.

Although this type of experiment cannot be carried out in a very short time, since fairly long counting times must be employed if reasonable accuracy is to be obtained with such weak sources, it is a very suitable project for school science societies, etc., and may usefully be extended over some years. It is, of course, vitally important that all equipment (especially liquid sample tubes) should be absolutely free from any contamination before being used for this work.

CHAPTER 8

Experiments Using Sealed Sources

A NUMBER of the experiments described in the previous chapter can be carried out with small sealed sources, e.g. the plotting of the characteristics of a Geiger tube, the statistics of counting and the plotting of an external beta absorption curve. The main purpose of this chapter is to give details of some experiments with small sealed sources which cannot be conveniently carried out with natural radioisotopes either because of the low specific activity of the latter or because they do not emit only one type of radiation.

Experiment 8.1. The Inverse Square Law Experiment for Gamma Radiation

The relationship between the gamma flux at a point and the distance of the source from that point is of great importance in health physics work apart from its general importance in physics.

A source of an activity of about 10 μcurie can be used in this experiment, although a rather more satisfactory experiment can be performed with a source of about 100 μcurie. A source of fairly high energy gamma rays (such as those from cobalt-60) is preferable to a source of low-energy gamma rays for use in this experiment.

It is not always very satisfactory to merely measure the distance of the source from the centre of the Geiger tube. The gamma photons produce electrons at the walls of the tube and it is these electrons which initiate counts. Owing to the non-linear effect of the inverse square law, the flux at the centre of the tube is less than the mean value of the flux at the walls. A 10 μcurie source of ^{60}Co will provide a total counting rate of about 100 counts/min (including background) in an MX168 tube at 50 cm. The background of an unshielded tube is about 45 counts/min, so for reasonable statistical accuracy in a short counting time, the maximum source to tube distance is little more than 50 cm. Other measurements must be made at shorter distances and errors in the source to tube distance measurement will be noticeable.

Use of a 100 μcurie Source

If a 100 μcurie source is to be used, the Geiger tube may be placed with its axis perpendicular to the direction of travel of the photons. Counts are taken at various distances, the distance being measured from the source to the centre of the Geiger tube. Reasonable counting rates can be obtained at distances of over 1 m and the errors in the distance measurements are a fairly small percentage of the whole distance.

If the corrected counting rate R and the source to tube distance d are related by an expression of the form

$$R = K d^n, \quad \text{where } K \text{ and } n \text{ are constants,}$$

$$\log_{10} R = n \log_{10} d + \log_{10} K.$$

Thus if one plots $\log_{10} R$ against $\log_{10} d$, the required value of n is equal to the slope of the graph obtained.

Use of a 10 μcurie Source

If a source of 10 μcurie or less is used, the distance d between the source and any fixed point on the tube is measured. The distance between the source and the tube used in the calculation is $(d + c)$, where c is a small constant but unknown correction to d. If the inverse square law is true, the corrected counting rate R is proportional to $1/(d + c)^2$

or $$\frac{1}{R^{\frac{1}{2}}} \propto (d + c).$$

Thus if the law is true, a graph of $R^{\frac{1}{2}}$ against d will be a straight line. The intercept of the graph on the d axis will be at the point $d = -c$. The orientation of the tube with respect to the direction of travel of the photons is unimportant if this method is used.

Although this second method does allow reasonable results to be obtained by the use of a weaker source, it does suffer from the disadvantage that the counting rates are merely shown to be compatible with the law instead of the law being derived from the measured counting rates.

Experiment 8.2. The Absorption of Gamma Radiation

Place an aluminium absorber of about 700 mg/cm² as near as possible to a Geiger tube window. Place a source of about 10 μcurie of a gamma emitter about 2 cm beneath the aluminium absorber. Count for about 2 min and repeat with lead absorbers of various thicknesses placed immediately above the source.

Plot a graph of $\log_{10}$(counting rate) against the absorber thickness in g/cm². From your graph find the absorption coefficient and the half-thickness for the absorption of the gamma radiation concerned in lead. If suitable gamma sources are available, repeat the measurements using isotopes which emit gamma rays of various energies. Cobalt-60 (mean energy 1·25 MeV) and caesium-137 (energy 0·662 MeV) are commonly used sources. If an isotope (or a mixture of isotopes) is available which emits gamma radiation of two very different energies, it will be possible to resolve the absorption curve into two components in a similar way to the beta absorption curve of Fig. 2.8 (p. 35). This is not possible in the case of gamma rays of similar energies such as the 1·17 and 1·33 MeV radiation from cobalt-60.

Experiment 8.3. The Decrease of Beta Flux with Source Distance

An experiment similar to the inverse square law experiment for gamma radiation may be carried out with an end-window

Geiger tube and a source of a few microcuries of a beta emitter. Measurements may be made over distances of up to about 1 or 2 m from the Geiger tube window except in the case of very low-energy beta emitters.

It will be found that the counting rate falls off with increasing distance at a faster rate than would be expected from the inverse square law alone. This is, of course, due to absorption of the radiation by the air (1 ft of air is about 40 mg/cm²).

Experiment 8.4. The Determination of the Resolving Time of Geiger Counting Equipment

For the determination of the resolving time of Geiger counting equipment of the order of 400 μsec, it is desirable to use two sources which each provide a counting rate of about 20,000 counts/min when placed at a convenient position near to the Geiger tube. It is just possible to use two sources of a uranium compound for this experiment, but the specific activity of these compounds is hardly great enough for the purpose. Two sources each containing a few microcuries of a beta emitter or a few hundred microcuries of a gamma emitter are much more convenient.

One of the sources is placed in position and is counted for an hour or more. Without touching or moving the first source, a second source is placed in a position where it alone will give a similar counting rate. The sources should not be close enough for either of them to reflect many of the particles emitted by the other. The two sources are counted together for about three-quarters of an hour. The first source is then removed without touching the second source. The second source is counted alone for about an hour. The background counting rate is measured over a period of about 10 min.

The counting of each source separately followed by the counting of the two sources together is not satisfactory, since the first source cannot be replaced exactly in the position it occupied previously. Let n_1 be the uncorrected counting rate of source 1 alone, n_2 be the uncorrected counting rate of source 2 alone, n_3 be the uncorrected combined counting rate, and n_b be the background counting rate.

Each of these counting rates may be corrected for resolving time losses in terms of the unknown resolving time τ. For example, the corrected counting rate for the first source is $n_1/(1 - n_1\tau)$. The sum of the counting rates due to the individual sources (after correction for resolving time losses) minus twice the background counting rate is equal to the corrected combined counting rate minus the background rate. That is:

$$\frac{n_1}{(1 - n_1\tau)} + \frac{n_2}{(1 - n_2\tau)} = \frac{n_3}{(1 - n_3\tau)} + \frac{n_b}{(1 - n_b\tau)}.$$

If this equation is multiplied by $(1 - n_1\tau)\ (1 - n_2\tau)\ (1 - n_3\tau)$ $(1 - n_b\tau)$ and identical terms are added or cancelled, one obtains $n_1 + n_2 - n_3 - n_b + 2\tau\ (n_3n_b - n_1n_2) + \tau^2\ (n_1n_2n_3 + n_1n_2n_b - n_1n_3n_b - n_2n_3n_b) = 0$. But $n_b \ll n_1$, n_2 or n_3.

Therefore

$$n_1 + n_2 - n_3 - n_b - 2n_1n_2\tau + n_1n_2n_3\tau^2 = 0.$$

Hence, solving this quadratic for τ:

$$\tau = \frac{1 - \sqrt{\left[1 - \dfrac{n_3}{n_1n_2}\ (n_1 + n_2 - n_3 - n_b)\right]}}{n_3}. \tag{8.1}$$

It has been shown[30] that the commonly used equation

$$\tau = \frac{n_1 + n_2 - n_3 - n_b}{2\ n_1n_2} \tag{8.2}$$

is not accurate at high counting rates, whereas low counting rates do not give the required statistical accuracy in the term $(n_1 + n_2 - n_3 - n_b)$. Equation (8.2) may be obtained by a binomial expansion of the square root term of eqn. (8.1) omitting all squared terms and those of higher indices. At counting rates of about 20,000 counts/min per source, eqn. (8.2) gives a result which is about 50 μsec too low when the resolving time is 400 μsec.

Experiment 8.5. Simple Gamma Radiography

Industrial gamma radiography is normally carried out with sources of the order of 1 curie. Reasonable radiographs can, however, be prepared in a school using a source of 1 mcurie or even less if the exposure time is increased in proportion.

Fasten a domestic water tap to an envelope wrapped fast X-ray film (e.g. Ilford type Industrial G) by means of plastic adhesive tape. Place the film at a distance of about 16 in. from a 1 mcurie source of caesium-137. The film should lie in a plane perpendicular to the direction of travel of the gamma photons. After about 1 week develop the film using the recommended darkroom illumination. A radiograph of quite reasonable clarity should be obtained. All of the internal parts of the tap including the threaded parts and any flaws in the metal should be clearly visible.

Further Comments

The radiation from caesium-137 has rather too high an energy to give the best contrast when a tap is used. Iridium-192 emits gamma rays of a lower energy, but is not so economical to purchase owing to its shorter half-life.

Caesium-137 sources of other activities may be used, the exposure time required being inversely proportional to the source strength and proportional to to the square of the source to film distance. The definition obtained decreases with decreasing source to film distance and with increasing source size. A large source will result in a penumbra being obtained around each part of the image. Fast films have a rather coarse grain, but if a finer grain film is used, the exposure time must be increased considerably.

CHAPTER 9

Experiments Using Unsealed Artificially Produced Isotopes

IN THIS chapter a few experiments involving the use of unsealed isotopes will be discussed. Although none of the isotopes employed are in the highest radiotoxicity grouping (class 1), stringent precautions should be taken to prevent contamination especially in a school. In educational establishments with very limited facilities, the purchase of isotopes in tablet form is the safest method.

Experiment 9.1. The Structure of the Thiosulphate Ion

One of the most important questions which arise when the structure of the thiosulphate ion, S_2O_3'', is being investigated concerns the equivalence or otherwise of the two sulphur atoms in the ion. If the sulphite ion SO_3'' takes up sulphur to become thiosulphate, does the incoming sulphur atom occupy a position in the ion similar to that of the original sulphur atom? This experiment attempts to answer the question by converting inactive sulphite ions into thiosulphate ions by the use of radioactive sulphur. Acid is then added to the thiosulphate so as to precipitate some sulphur and convert the remainder into sulphur dioxide.

$$S_2O_3'' + 2HCl \longrightarrow SO_2 + S + 2Cl' + H_2O.$$

If the radioactivity is all present in either the sulphur dioxide or in the precipitated sulphur, this shows that the radioactive sulphur did not occupy a similar position in the thiosulphate ion as the sulphur atoms present in the initial sulphite ions. If, however, half of the activity is present in the gas and the other half in the precipitated sulphur, this tends to indicate that the two sulphur atoms occupy similar positions in the thiosulphate ion; it does not prove this, since radioactive sulphur atoms may undergo exchange with inactive ones in another position in the ion.

First prepare some finely divided radioactive sulphur in the following way. Dissolve about $0 \cdot 25$ g of sulphur containing about $0 \cdot 1$–1 μcurie of ^{35}S in 10 ml of carbon disulphide and decant the clear solution from any residue. Precipitate the sulphur by adding a solvent such as acetone (about 20 ml). Remove the supernatent liquid with a small suction tube and place it in a liquid radioactive waste container. Wash the precipitated sulphur with a few millilitres of acetone and then with a few millilitres of water, discarding the liquids into the radioactive waste container.

Place the radioactive sulphur in a 100 ml flask with 30 ml of a solution containing $2 \cdot 1$ g of sodium sulphite (equivalent to $4 \cdot 2$ g of sodium sulphite crystals, $Na_2SO_3 \cdot 7H_2O$). Fit a rubber stopper connected to a Bunsen valve to the flask. Gently boil the mixture in a heating mantle until all of the sulphur has dissolved. The Bunsen valve prevents air from entering the flask and oxidising the sulphite to sulphate. Cool the flask. Remove the bung and replace it with a stopper containing three holes. A dropping funnel containing dilute hydrochloric acid passes through one of the holes, an air inlet through another, whilst the third is connected to a wash bottle containing saturated barium hydroxide solution ("baryta"); the other side of the wash bottle is connected to an aspirator. Draw air slowly through the apparatus and add 10–20 ml of hydrochloric acid (2 N) from the dropping funnel. Heat the solution in the flask to expel all the dissolved sulphur dioxide.

Filter off the precipitate of barium sulphite formed in the baryta solution by the evolved sulphur dioxide, place the precipitate in a planchet and count. Filter off the sulphur formed by the addition of the acid to the contents of the flask, transfer to a planchet and count.

It will be found that virtually all of the activity is present in the precipitated sulphur and hardly any in the barium sulphite. Thus the sulphur atoms which are liberated by the addition of the acid are the same atoms as those which were taken up by the sulphite. Therefore the two sulphur atoms in the thiosulphate ion do not occupy equivalent positions. The thiosulphate ion may be represented as

$$\left[\begin{array}{c} O \\ \| \\ O = S = S^* \\ \| \\ O \end{array} \right]''$$

where S* denotes the radioactive sulphur atom. However there are a number of similar forms resonating with one another, so the position of the single and double bonds has no real meaning.

Experiment 9.2. The Dynamic Equilibrium between a Metal and its Ions

The equilibrium between a metal and its ions is fundamental in the theory of electrochemistry. This experiment shows that the equilibrium is a dynamic one.

Take about 3 ml of a solution containing about 3 μcurie of ^{65}Zn as zinc chloride and add dilute ammonia drop by drop until the pH is about 5. Clean some zinc granules of diameter about 0·5 mm in very dilute hydrochloric acid and wash them with water. Add about 1 g of the granules to the radioactive zinc chloride solution. After an interval of about 15 min, decant the solution and wash the granules with water and then with alcohol. Place them in a planchet and dry them under an infrared lamp. Check that they are evenly spread in the planchet before counting them. This procedure may be repeated using the same radioactive zinc chloride solution to ascertain whether the activity of the zinc increases with the time for which it is in contact with the solution.

If the granules are left in contact with the solution overnight, they may be used in the following part of the experiment.

Add about 1 g of the active zinc granules to 15 ml of inactive zinc chloride (about $0 \cdot 5$ M) if a 10 ml liquid sample tube is to be used or add the granules to 10 ml of zinc chloride solution if a 5 ml liquid sample tube is to be used. After about 15 min decant the solution into a liquid sample tube and take a short count. Return the solution to the zinc granules immediately and take further counts initially at 15 min intervals, but later the intervals may be increased. Plot a graph of the activity of the solution against $\log_{10}$ (time). Do you feel your results may indicate that the rate of exchange of zinc atoms with zinc ions decreases exponentially with the depth of the atoms beneath the surface of the metal?

The second part of the experiment may be repeated with an alcoholic solution of zinc chloride, but care must be taken to prevent excessive evaporation.

Experiment 9.3. Coprecipitation and Adsorption

Coprecipitation

In this experiment the percentage of phosphate, iodide and caesium in carrier-free concentrations which are coprecipitated with barium sulphate is determined.

Evaporate 1 ml of a solution containing about $0 \cdot 1$ μcurie/ml of ^{32}P as inorganic orthophosphate to dryness in a planchet using an infrared lamp. Count under an end-window tube. Add 1 ml of the same ^{32}P solution to 2 ml of a solution containing about $0 \cdot 05$ g of barium chloride. Heat nearly to the boiling point and precipitate the barium with 5 ml of dilute sulphuric acid. Filter off the precipitate and wash, first with a little dilute sulphuric acid, then with water and finally with alcohol. Dry and count. Calculate the percentage of ^{32}P which has been coprecipitated.

Repeat the experiment by adding 1 ml of the ^{32}P to 2 ml of a solution containing $0 \cdot 05$ g of barium chloride and $0 \cdot 05$ g of sodium phosphate as a hold-back carrier.

The experiments may be repeated with other materials, for example, with a solution of ^{131}I as iodide and potassium iodide as hold-back carrier. If the experiment is carried out with ^{137}Cs, note whether separation of the daughter product ^{137m}Ba has occurred. This daughter isotope decays with a 2·6 min half-life.

Adsorption

In this part of the experiment the percentage of various radio-active ions adsorbed on a preformed precipitate of barium sulphate is estimated.

Add 5 ml of dilute sulphuric acid to 2 ml of a solution containing 0·05 g of barium chloride. Heat to the boiling point. Add 1 ml of one of the radioisotope solutions used previously and boil for about 1 min. Filter and count the precipitate. Repeat using 1 ml of the radionuclide solution containing 0·05 g of hold-back carrier.

Similar experiments may be carried out using a ferric or aluminium hydroxide precipitate instead of barium sulphate. One millilitre of ferric chloride or aluminium sulphate containing 0·05 g of the material is used instead of barium chloride and 5 ml of dilute ammonia is used as the precipitant.

Try to ascertain whether potassium or sodium ions are effective as hold-back carriers for caesium ions or whether bromide ions can be used as hold-back carriers for iodide ions.

Experiment 9.4. The Preparation of a Labelled Compound

Iodoform labelled with ^{131}I atoms may be prepared in the following way. Dissolve 1 g of iodine in 5 ml of alcohol and add about 0·5 μcurie of ^{131}I as iodide. The iodide undergoes exchange with the iodine atoms. Evaporate 1 ml of the solution to dryness in a stream of air in a fume cupboard and count the specimen.

Dissolve 2 g of sodium carbonate crystals in 10 ml of water and add 3 ml of the active alcoholic iodine solution. Keep the mixture at about 70°C for a few minutes and then cool. Filter off the crystals of iodoform, wash them with a little water and allow them to dry in a stream of air in a warm place. Count the specimen. What fraction of the iodine has been converted into iodoform?

Warm the liquid from which the iodoform crystals were obtained to about 70°C and pass a little chlorine through the solution. This liberates iodine from the sodium iodide present and results in the formation of more iodoform. Allow the solution to cool, collect the crystals and measure their activity.

Experiment 9.5. The Absorption of Phosphorus by a Plant

Place a plant which is about 8 in. high in 50 ml of water containing about 5 μcurie of ^{32}P (possibly with about 20 mg of sodium dihydrogen orthophosphate as a carrier). It does not matter whether the plant has roots or whether its cut stem is placed in the solution.

After 1 or 2 days remove the plant and cut off the lower parts which have been immersed in the solution. Place a piece of cellophane or very thin polythene sheet on an envelope wrapped X-ray film and put the top part of the plant on the sheet. Press the plant flat against it by placing a fairly heavy object with a flat lower surface on it. After 1 or 2 days process the film. It is possible to obtain very good negatives in this way which show the major veins of the leaf as dark lines, since the concentration of the phosphorus is greater there than elsewhere. A large concentration of phosphorus is normally present in the stem.

An alternative experiment may be carried out by injecting about 1 μcurie of ^{32}P dissolved in about 0·1 ml of water into the stem of a plant. A celery stalk is especially convenient. The plant may be immersed in water or alternatively a potted plant may be used. If the position of the ^{32}P is found periodically with an end-window Geiger tube, almost all of it will be found above the point of injection. Eventually the isotope will be found in all parts of the plant at points above the level of injection.

The study of the uptake of radionuclides by plants is of importance in connection with fallout hazards.

Experiment 9.6. The Absorption of Phosphorus by Yeast

Weigh 2 g of dry yeast and add it to 30 ml of a dilute sugar solution containing about 2 μcurie of ^{32}P. Allow the mixture to stand overnight at a temperature of about 30°C. Filter off the yeast and wash it with water. After drying the yeast, measure the activity of 0·5 g of it evenly spread on a planchet. Evaporate 5 ml of the filtrate to dryness and measure its activity.

Find the accumulation factor which is defined as

$$\frac{\text{Activity of 1 g of yeast}}{\text{Activity of 1 g of the solution}}.$$

A greater degree of accuracy would be obtained by igniting the yeast so that no self-absorption would occur in the counting of this material.

Problems

1. Write equations for the following changes:

(a) β^- decay of $^{40}_{19}K$.

(b) α decay of $^{239}_{94}Pu$.

(c) β^+ decay of $^{22}_{11}Na$.

(d) The reaction of an atom of $^{32}_{16}S$ with a neutron to form $^{32}_{15}P$.

(e) An atom reacts with a single neutron to form an atom of $^{14}_{6}C$ and a proton.

2. Find the activity in microcuries of the ^{232}Th in 1 g of thorium oxide, ThO_2. Calculate the activity of the ^{208}Tl in the sample if it is in equilibrium with the thorium. (Avogadro's number $= 6 \cdot 023 \times 10^{23}$; use the data in Fig. 3.2 on p. 44.)

[*Answers:* 0·09605 and 0·03237 μcurie.]

3. Calculate the volume of radon gas measured at N.T.P. in equilibrium with 1 g of elemental radium. What is the total volume of radon produced per year? (Avogadro's number $= 6 \cdot 023 \times 10^{23}$; the gram-molecular volume $= 22 \cdot 4$ l.; use the data in Fig. 3.1 on p. 44.)

[*Answers:* $6 \cdot 41 \times 10^{-4}$ cc and 0·043 cc at N.T.P.]

4. 10 ml of a solution containing a radioisotope is evaporated to dryness and is found to give a counting rate of 14,410 counts/min. One millilitre of the same solution counted with the same geometry gives a counting rate of 1560 counts/min. What is the resolving time of the equipment?

[*Answer:* 353 μsec.]

5. An isotope has a half-life of 40 min. A sample of this nuclide provides an initial counting rate of 20,000 counts/min. What will the counting rate be after 25 min (a) if the resolving time is negligible, and (b) if the resolving time is 400 μsec?

[*Answers:* (a) 12,970 counts/min, and (b) 13,610 counts/min.]

6. A Geiger counter records 1000 counts in 40 min with a sample in position and 240 counts in 30 min when the background rate is being determined. What is the net sample counting rate and its standard deviation?

[*Answer:* $17 \pm 0 \cdot 94$ counts/min.]

7. At what distance could a missing 1 mcurie source of ^{60}Co be detected with a portable monitor which can detect $0 \cdot 25$ mrad/hr?

[*Answer:* $2 \cdot 29$ m.]

8. For how long could a schoolboy work at 2 ft from a source of 10 μcurie of ^{137}Cs before receiving the maximum permissible annual dose of 50 mrad if only the gamma radiation escapes?

[*Answer:* 5992 hr.]

9. Describe how you would try to identify an unknown beta emitter.

10. The table shows the decay of a radioisotope with time. If the resolving time of the equipment was negligible and the background counting rate was 45 per min, calculate the half-life of the isotope.

Time (hr)	0	1	2	3	4	5	6	7	8	9
Counts/min	2336	1547	1204	793	659	466	344	231	193	137

11. A liquid sample counting tube has a liquid sample volume of 10 ml and an efficiency of $1 \cdot 5 \%$ for a certain isotope. What must be the concentration of that isotope if a counting rate of 100 counts/min above the background is to be obtained?

[*Answer:* $3 \cdot 00 \times 10^{-4}$ μcurie/ml.]

12. A little thoron was placed in a quartz fibre ionisation chamber instrument and the following readings were obtained. Deduce the half-life of thoron.

Time (sec)	0	10	20	30	40	50	60
Reading ("rad")	0	0·04	0·08	0·11	0·14	0·17	0·19

Time (sec)	80	100	120	140	150	180	210
Reading ("rad")	0·23	0·26	0·28	0·29	0·30	0·32	0·33

Regulations on the Use of Radioisotopes in United Kingdom Educational Establishments

DURING the past few years various regulations have been brought into force controlling the use of radioactive materials and X-rays in British educational establishments. An administrative Memorandum[31] issued by the Ministry of Education in 1957 required technical colleges to inform the Ministry well in advance before commencing work with radioactive materials. Two booklets were issued by the Ministry for the guidance of technical colleges undertaking such work.[14, 32] A further Ministry of Education Memorandum appeared in 1958 which required schools to apply for special authorisation if they wished to use any radioactive materials other than potassium, uranium or thorium salts in forms normally available for purchase.[33] A series of notes for guidance of schools and forms of application for special authorisation were made available.

In December 1963 the Radioactive Substances Act, 1960 (which is administered by the Ministry of Housing and Local Government), came into force[34], [35] and about the same time the Radioactive Substances (Schools, etc.) Exemption Order[36] was approved. In September 1964 a *Code of Practice for the Protection of Persons Exposed to Ionising Radiation in Research and Teaching* [13] was published by the Ministry of Labour. This code does not normally apply to schools or to establishments of further education which are carrying out radioisotope work at a level not above that permitted in schools. In January 1965 an Administrative Memorandum[7] was issued by the Ministry of Education stating the requirements for the use of sources of ionising radiation in schools and establishments of further education.

The following summary of regulations which apply to the use of radioisotopes in educational establishments (which are necessarily somewhat complicated) is very much abbreviated. These regulations may change from time to time. Reference must therefore be made to the appropriate regulations themselves for the precise terms applying to any educational establishment.

The Radioactive Substances Act, 1960

Under section 1 of the Radioactive Substances Act no person may keep or use (or permit to be kept or used) any radioactive material on premises which are used for the purpose of an undertaking carried on by him unless he is registered or exempted.

Section 1 relates to premises, but application may be made under section 3 of the Act for registration of mobile radioactive apparatus to be used on any premises (under certain conditions). A person who gives lecture demonstrations at various places may wish to apply for registration under this section of the Act.

Under section 6 of the Act no person may dispose of any radioactive waste or permit its disposal on or from any premises which are used for the purposes of an undertaking carried on by him except in accordance with an authorisation. An authorisation is also required for the accumulation of radioactive waste on any premises.

When an application for registration or an authorisation under the Act is made, it is usual for one of the Radiochemical Inspectors of the Ministry of Housing to visit the premises concerned and to make recommendations as to the terms of the registration. Limitations are imposed on the maximum amount of radioactive material which may be kept on any premises and on the rate at which radioactive material may be disposed of in specified ways. Copies of the certificates of registration must be posted on the premises where they can conveniently be read by persons who work there.

G

Appendix 1

Exemptions

Many common items are slightly radioactive and, in order to avoid unnecessary administrative work, certain exemptions are granted from registration or authorisation under the Act under specified conditions. For example, the keeping and use of the luminous radioactive material on the faces of clocks and watches and the disposal of this material is exempt from registration and authorisation except on premises where clocks and watches are manufactured or repaired.

The following Exemption Orders are those which are considered to be of greatest interest in educational establishments.

The Radioactive Substances (Testing Instruments) Exemption Order

This order grants conditional exemption from registration for the keeping and use (except for exhibition purposes or on the manufacturer's premises) of sealed sources which contain not more than 100 μcurie (including decay products) and which are incorporated in or accompany any instruments designed for investigating or testing the characteristics of substances or articles. Mobile apparatus consisting of such sources is also granted exemption. The disposal of such sources by return to the manufacturers or (where the total activity does not exceed 5 μcurie and not more than ten such sources are disposed of per week) by the local authority refuse service is also exempt.

The Radioactive Substances (Prepared Uranium and Thorium Compounds) Exemption Order

This order applies to prepared compounds of uranium and thorium from which each of the radioactive decay products has been substantially removed in the course of preparation. Their use for demonstrating or investigating the characteristics of any materials is exempt from registration provided that not more than 2 kg of uranium and thorium in aggregate are held on the premises. Conditional exemption is also given for the disposal of waste arising from these prepared compounds provided that not more than a total of 100 g per day of uranium and thorium is disposed of as solid or liquid waste and 1 g per day as gaseous waste.

The Radioactive Substances (Schools, etc.)
Exemption Order

This order applies to maintained, direct grant and independent schools recognised by the Ministry of Education as efficient and to most establishments of further education including most teacher-training colleges. The order allows the conditional keeping and use of radioactive material without registration and the conditional disposal of radioactive waste. The main conditions applying under this order are:

1. Not more than 4 mcurie of exempt radioactive material may be kept on the premises at any time. In the case of sealed sources, decay products are not counted in the total amount.
2. Not more than 2 mcurie of radioactive material in the form of open sources (including any decay products) may be brought onto the premises in any four consecutive weeks or kept there at any time. Open sources must not contain any alpha emitters or strontium–90.
3. No sealed source may be mutilated or any material (whether active or not) removed from it.
4. If it is believed or suspected that an exempted source has been lost or stolen, the police and the Ministry of Housing and Local Government must be informed as soon as possible.
5. The Ministry of Housing and Local Government must be informed if it is suspected that a closed source has been damaged or if radioactive material is suspected to be leaking from it.
6. Records must be kept for inspection by the Ministry of Housing and Local Government. These records must show the date on which any exempted source was brought onto the premises, the date when it was removed and the name

of the occupier and the address of the premises to which it was removed. They must also show the name and the total activity of each of the nuclides present (except for the decay products formed in closed sources) in the source at the time it was brought onto the premises and at the time it was removed.

The main conditions applying to the disposal of radioactive waste under the Schools Exemption Order are:

1. The waste must be disposed of as soon as practicable.
2. Waste closed sources may be returned to the manufacturers of such sources or to persons such as instrument manufacturers who are authorised to accept waste sources for disposal.
3. A maximum of 10 μcurie per week of solid waste may be disposed of through the local authority refuse service or at a tip used for the disposal of substantial quantities of normal refuse provided that, immediately before the waste is disposed of, it is in one or more containers in each of which the volume of refuse is not less than 3 ft^3. The total amount of waste (including any decay products) must not exceed 10 μcurie and the activity in any one article of the waste must not exceed 1 μcurie.
4. Liquid waste from exempt sources may be disposed of through the normal drainage system provided that the total amount per week does not exceed 500 μcurie.
5. Gaseous waste from an exempt source of up to 1 μcurie/day may be allowed to escape into the open air.

Levels of Work

It is the responsibility of local education authorities in the case of maintained establishments and of governing bodies in the case of establishments which are not maintained or assisted by local authorities to take precautions to protect persons who might be exposed to radiation in the establishments whether in the course of their work or otherwise. The stringency of these precautions will depend on the level of the work being undertaken and on the amount and type of the isotopes used.

The main distinction is drawn between establishments carrying out work at "schools level" (which will be defined later) and those carrying out work at a higher level. Those working at schools level will normally have no difficulty in complying with the provisions of the Radioactive Substances (Schools, etc.) Exemption Order and will therefore not need to be registered under the Radioactive Substances Act. Educational establishments working at a higher level may need to be registered under section 1 of the Act to keep radioactive substances and authorised under section 6 of the Act to dispose of waste. In certain exceptional circumstances a school may be registered under the Act; for example, if it has a neutron source.

Work which is carried out at the "higher level" will be controlled by the *Code of Practice for the Protection of Persons Exposed to Ionising Radiation in Research and Teaching*.[13] This code describes in detail the administrative organisation which must be set up in an establishment to which the code applies including the appointment of radiological safety officers. It also gives details of the requirements for medical supervision, of the precautions required in the use of X-ray equipment, etc.

Approval by the Secretary of State

The following paragraph has been included in the regulations governing the conduct of maintained and direct grant schools and of maintained and assisted colleges:

"No instruction shall be given in the school or educational establishment involving the use of
  (i) radioactive material other than a compound of potassium, thorium or uranium normally used as a chemical agent or
  (ii) apparatus in which electrons are accelerated by a potential difference of 5 kilovolts or greater other than

apparatus used only for the purpose of receiving visua
images by way of television

unless the Secretary of State has given his approval to the giving
of such instruction, which approval he may withdraw if at any
time he is of the opinion that the arrangements made for the
health and safety of the pupils and staff are inadequate."

Applications for individual approval should be made by the
controlling authority of the establishment (local authority
governing body or proprietor) on form I.R.N. if it is desired to
work at schools level. If, however, the work of the establishment
with radioisotopes will include only those experiments set out in
the report on the *Teaching of Modern Physics*,[37] application
should be made on the simpler form I.R.N. (Certificate). These
forms can be obtained from the Department of Education and
Science, Architects and Building Branch, Curzon Street, London
W. 1. Colleges intending to work under the full provisions of the
Code of Practice[13] must also make application to the Department of Education and Science. A college whose use of radioactive
substances falls within the limits of exemption of the *Code*[13] and
in which no equipment is used for accelerating electrons to
energies of 5 kV or more need not apply for approval by the
Secretary of State. The main exemptions of the code include the
use of natural uranium or natural thorium in quantities up to
10 kg and the conditional use of sealed sources, the dose rate at the
surface of which does not exceed 10 mrad/hr.

It is important to note that prior approval by the Secretary of
State is required in most cases. Application should be made well
in advance. The Department of Education and Science requests
colleges to inform them at least 6 months before work with
radioisotopes is commenced. Early application is also necessary
for registration or authorisation under the Radioactive Substances Act.

Schools Level

"Schools level" means approximately the standard reached in
courses up to the General Certificate of Education at Advanced

Level, Ordinary National Certificate, etc.[17] The work likely to be carried out at present can be classified into two main types:[17]

(i) The work suggested in the report on *The Teaching of Modern Physics.*[37]

(ii) Other work involving the use of unsealed sources in addition to sealed sources.

A school or college which has obtained the approval of the Secretary of State to carry out work at schools level must comply with the terms of the notes I.R.N.[17] (or I.R.X. in the case of X-ray equipment) in order to satisfy the Schools Regulations, 1959. Some of the main provisions of the notes I.R.N. are:

1. Pupils below the age of 16 years will in no circumstances be allowed to conduct experiments with open or closed sources except those consisting of potassium, natural uranium or thorium or certain very weak sources of an activity less than $0 \cdot 1$ μcurie in which the active material is firmly bound to an inactive support. Neither will pupils under the age of 16 be allowed in laboratories in which other pupils are conducting radioisotope experiments.

2. Teachers' qualifications.

   Any science teacher will normally be allowed to conduct experiments with potassium, natural uranium or natural thorium compounds, with closed sources of an activity up to 10 μcurie (which are manufactured to a specification approved by the Department of Education and Science) and with very weak sources of an activity not greater than $0 \cdot 1$ μcurie in which the active material is firmly bonded to an inactive surface.

   Where other radioactive substances are concerned, consideration will be given to the qualifications of individual members of staff by the Secretary of State. Normally a degree in science or a pass in science as a main subject at a teacher-training college or a comparable qualification will be required and, in addition, the teacher will be required to have undergone a course of instruction in health physics and in laboratory work with open and closed sources. The course of instruction may be part of a course leading to the initial qualification or a separate course of not less than 25 hr duration. In certain cases other requirements may be necessary.

3. Establishments whose applications have been approved can obtain, from any supplier of such sources, closed sources which contain up to 10 μcurie of radioactive material and which are manufactured according to a specification of the Department of Education and Science. A list of these sources will be supplied by the Department on request.

   Closed sources of greater activity and all open sources may be obtained only from the Radiochemical Centre, Amersham, Buckinghamshire.

4. No establishment may hold at any one time a total of more than 4 mcurie of open and closed sources of which not more than 2 mcurie may be open sources. No alpha emitters or strontium-90 may be kept as open sources.

5. No pupil shall receive more than 50 mrad of external radiation in any one year as a result of experiments in educational establishments.

6. Maximum permissible quantities of unsealed isotopes per experiment.

   The maximum permissible quantity of an unsealed radio isotope which may be used in any experiment is one-tenth of the amount of that isotope which, according to the recommendations of the International Committee on Radiological Protection,[15] is the acceptable limit for ingestion by an occupational worker in a year.

   The maximum permissible quantity per experiment may be calculated in the following way, taking I^{131} as an example. The maximum permissible concentration in drinking water is 2×10^{-5} μcurie/c.c.[15] The daily intake of water assumed to be 2·2 l and therefore the maximum intake for an occupationally exposed worker is $4·4 \times 10^{-2}$ μcurie/da or 16 μcurie/year. The maximum permissible amount per experiment is therefore 1·6 μcurie.

Examples of maximum permissible amounts per experiment are:[17]

Beta/gamma emitters		*Beta emitters*	
(μcurie)		(μcurie)	
^{24}Na	160	^{32}P	16
^{42}K	240	^{35}S	48
^{110m}Ag	24	^{36}Cl	64
^{131}I	1·6	^{14}C	640

If more than one nuclide is used in any experiment, the maximum permissible amount of each is reduced. For example, half the maximum permissible amount of ^{32}P (8 μcurie) may be used with half the maximum permissible amount of ^{14}C (320 μcurie). These are maximum amounts; most experiments can be performed with much smaller quantities.

7. Maximum amounts which may be kept.

The maximum total amount of an unsealed nuclide which may be kept at any time is 5 times the maximum permissible amount per experiment or 2 mcuries, whichever is the smaller. For example if 80 μcurie of ^{32}P is kept, no other unsealed isotopes may be stored. If more than one nuclide is kept in the form of open sources, the maximum quantity of each should be calculated on a weighted *pro rata* basis. For example, the maximum amount stored may be made up of 320 μcurie of ^{24}Na, 48 μcurie of ^{110m}Ag and 16 μcurie of ^{32}P. This is twice the maximum permissible amount of ^{24}Na per experiment, twice that of ^{110m}Ag plus the maximum permissible amount of ^{32}P per experiment; thus the total is 5 times the maximum permissible amount per experiment.

8. No attempt may be made to concentrate radium or meso-thorium from uranium or thorium ores. Neither may any material be removed from luminous dials or radioactive luminous paint be purchased.

9. All radioactive material for which approval has been obtained should be kept in a locked and marked store or cupboard. The local fire service should be notified of the location of the store. The store or cupboard should be away from all permanently occupied spaces and the dose rate immediately outside it should be calculated or measured and marked on the store.

10. Various recommendations are made in notes I.R.N. on the precautions to be adopted when using unsealed radioisotopes. Most of these are quoted in Chapter 4.

Transport of Radioisotopes

There are no regulations at the present time covering the transport of small amounts of radioactive materials in private cars, but suitable regulations are being prepared by the Ministry of Transport.

APPENDIX 2

Radioisotope Data

THE following table provides data on the half-lives and particle energies of some of the radioisotopes commonly used in educational or other work. The numbers in brackets show the percentage of particles emitted of the stated energy.

Symbol	Half-life	Alpha or beta energy (MeV)	Gamma energy (MeV)	Specific gamma ray emission (rad/hr/mc at 1 cm)
$^3_1$H	12·26 yr	$\beta-$ 0·0186 (100)	None	
$^{14}_6$C	5570 yr	$\beta-$ 0·158 (100)	None	
$^{22}_{11}$Na	2·58 yr	$\beta+$ 0·54 (90) E.C. (10)	1·28 (100)	12·0

Symbol	Half-life	Alpha or beta energy (MeV)	Gamma energy (MeV)	Specific gamma ray emission (rad/hr/mc at 1 cm)
$^{24}_{11}$Na	15·0 hr	β^- 1·39	2·75 (100); 1·37 (100)	18·5
$^{32}_{15}$P	14·3 d	β^- 1·71	None	
$^{35}_{16}$S	87 d	β^- 0·167	None	
$^{36}_{17}$Cl	3 × 10⁵ yr	β^- 0·71 (98) E.C. (2)	None	
$^{40}_{19}$K	1·27 × 10⁹ yr	β^- 1·32 (89) E.C. (11)	1·46 (11)	
$^{42}_{19}$K	12·4 hr	β^- 3·55 (82) 2·03 (18)	1·52 (18)	1·4
$^{45}_{20}$Ca	160 d	β^- 0·25 (100)	None	
$^{51}_{24}$Cr	27·8 d	E.C. (100)	0·32 (10)	0·15
$^{54}_{25}$Mn	280 d	E.C. (100)	0·84 (100)	4·7
$^{60}_{27}$Co	5·27 yr	β^- 0·31 (100)	1·33 (100); 1·17 (100)	13·1
$^{65}_{30}$Zn	245 d	E.C. (98) β^+ 0·33 (2)	1·11 (50)	2·7
$^{87}_{37}$Rb	4·8 × 10¹⁰ yr	β^- 0·275	None	

$^{90}_{38}$Sr	28 yr	$\beta-$ 0·54 (100)	(In equilibrium with ^{90}Y)	
$^{90}_{39}$Y	64·2 hr	$\beta-$ 2·27 (100)		1·7
$^{106}_{44}$Ru	1·00 yr	$\beta-$ 0·04 (100)	(In equilibrium with ^{106}Rh)	14·3
$^{106}_{45}$Rh	30 sec	$\beta-$ 3·53 (72)	Various gamma	
$^{110m}_{47}$Ag	253 d	$\beta-$ 0·086 (55), etc.	Various gamma	
$^{109}_{48}$Cd	1·3 yr	E.C. (100)	(In equilibrium with ^{109}Ag)	2·2
$^{113}_{50}$Sn	112 d	E.C. (100)	0·255 (2) (Forms ^{113m}In)	
$^{132}_{52}$Te	78 hr	$\beta-$ 0·22 (60)	0·23 (100); 0·053 (100)	2·2
$^{128}_{53}$I	25·0 min	$\beta-$ 2·12 (76), etc.	Various gamma	
$^{131}_{53}$I	8·06 d	$\beta-$ 0·61 (87), etc.	0·364 (82); 0·64 (9); 0·284 (6), etc.	2·2
$^{132}_{53}$I	2·3 hr	$\beta-$ 1·53 (24) 1·16 (23) 2·12 (18)	0·67 (100); 0·78 (80); 0·53 (30); 0·96 (21), etc.	11·8
$^{137}_{55}$Cs	30 yr	$\beta-$ 0·51 (92) 1·17 (8)	(In equilibrium with ^{137m}Ba)	3·1 from daughter
$^{137m}_{56}$Ba	2·6 min	—	0·662 (100)	3·1
$^{144}_{58}$Ce	285 d	$\beta-$ 0·32 (72); 0·19 (20)	0·034–0·134 (In equilibrium with ^{144}Pr)	

Symbol	Half-life	Alpha or beta energy (MeV)	Gamma energy (MeV)	Specific gamma ray emission (rad/hr/mc at 1 cm)
$^{144}_{59}$Pr	17·4 min	$\beta-$ 2·98 (98)	0·69 (1·6); 2·18 (0·8)	
$^{170}_{69}$Tm	129 d	$\beta-$ 0·96 (78) 0·88 (22)	0·084 (3)	0·025
$^{192}_{77}$Ir	74 d	$\beta-$ 0·67 (41) 0·53 (38)	0·316; 0·468; 0·309; 0·296; etc.	4·8
$^{198}_{79}$Au	2·70 d	$\beta-$ 0·96 (99); 0·28 (1)	0·412 (99), etc.	2·3
$^{204}_{81}$Tl	3·9 yr	$\beta-$ 0·77 (98)	None	
$^{208}_{81}$Tl	3·1 min	$\beta-$ 1·80 (47), etc.	2·61 (100); 0·58 (77); 0·51 (31), etc.	
$^{210}_{82}$Pb	20 yr	$\beta-$ 0·017 (85); 0·063 (15)	0·046 (10)	
$^{212}_{82}$Pb	10·64 hr	$\beta-$ 0·34 (84); 0·58 (12)	0·239 (83), etc.	
$^{212}_{83}$Bi	60·5 min	$\beta-$ 2·25 (64) α 6·09 (36)	0·04 (25), etc.	
$^{212}_{84}$Po	0·30 μsec	α 8·78		
$^{220}_{86}$Rn	55 sec	α 6·28 (99)	0·54 (0·3)	
$^{222}_{86}$Rn	3·823 d	α 5·49 (99)		

$^{224}_{88}Ra$	3·64 d	α	5·68 (95); 5·44 (5)	0·241 (5)
$^{226}_{88}Ra$	1620 yr	α	4·78 (95); 4·59 (4)	0·187 (4) 8·25 in equilibrium
$^{228}_{88}Ra$	6·7 yr	β−	0·03 approx.	
$^{227}_{89}Ac$	21·6 yr	β− 0·046 (99); α 4·94 (1)		
$^{228}_{89}Ac$	6·13 hr	β−	1·11 (53), etc.	Various gamma
$^{228}_{90}Th$	1·91 yr	α	5·42 (71); 5·34 (28)	Various gamma
$^{230}_{90}Th$	8 × 10⁴ yr	α	4·68 (76); 4·61 (24)	Various gamma
$^{231}_{90}Th$	25·6 hr	β−	0·30	Various gamma
$^{232}_{90}Th$	1·41 × 10¹⁰ yr	α	4·01 (76); 3·95 (24)	0·059 (24)
$^{234}_{90}Th$	24·1 d	β−	0·19 (65); 0·10 (35)	Various gamma
$^{231}_{91}Pa$	3·3 × 10⁴ yr	α	5·00 (24), etc.	0·038–0·29
$^{234m}_{91}Pa$	1·18 min	β− 2·31 (99); I.T. (1)		Various gamma
$^{234}_{91}Pa$	6·66 hr	β−	1·13	Various gamma
$^{234}_{92}U$	2·50 × 10⁵ yr	α	4·77 (72); 4·72 (28)	Various gamma

Symbol	Half-life	Alpha or beta energy (MeV)	Gamma energy (MeV)	Specific gamma ray emission (rad/hr/mc at 1 cm)
$^{235}_{92}$U	$7 \cdot 1 \times 10^8$ yr	α $4 \cdot 18$–$4 \cdot 56$	$0 \cdot 185$ (55), etc.	
$^{238}_{92}$U	$4 \cdot 51 \times 10^9$ yr	α $4 \cdot 19$	$0 \cdot 048$ (23)	
$^{239}_{94}$Pu	24,300 yr	α $5 \cdot 15$ (72) $5 \cdot 12$ (17) $5 \cdot 10$ (11)	$0 \cdot 013$ (17), etc.	
$^{241}_{95}$Am	458 yr	α $5 \cdot 48$ (85) $5 \cdot 44$ (13)	Various gamma	

APPENDIX 3

Table of Resolving Time Corrections for a Dead Time of 400 Microseconds

Counts/ min	Lost counts	Counts/ min	Lost counts	Counts/ min	Lost counts
20,000	3,079	18,500	2,604	17,000	2,174
19,950	3,063	18,450	2,590	16,950	2,162
19,900	3,045	18,400	2,573	16,900	2,147
19,850	3,029	18,350	2,559	16,850	2,134
19,800	3,014	18,300	2,545	16,800	2,121
19,750	2,996	18,250	2,529	16,750	2,106
19,700	2,980	18,200	2,515	16,700	2,094
19,650	2,965	18,150	2,501	16,650	2,081
19,600	2,947	18,100	2,485	16,600	2,066
19,550	2,932	18,050	2,471	16,550	2,054
19,500	2,916	18,000	2,455	16,500	2,041
19,450	2,899	17,950	2,441	16,450	2,027
19,400	2,883	17,900	2,427	16,400	2,015
19,350	2,868	17,850	2,414	16,350	2,002
19,300	2,851	17,800	2,397	16,300	1,988
19,250	2,836	17,750	2,384	16,250	1,976
19,200	2,821	17,700	2,370	16,200	1,963
19,150	2,803	17,650	2,355	16,150	1,949
19,100	2,789	17,600	2,341	16,100	1,937
19,050	2,774	17,550	2,328	16,050	1,925
19,000	2,757	17,500	2,312	16,000	1,911
18,950	2,742	17,450	2,299	15,950	1,899
18,900	2,727	17,400	2,285	15,900	1,887
18,850	2,710	17,350	2,270	15,850	1,873
18,800	2,696	17,300	2,257	15,800	1,862
18,750	2,681	17,250	2,244	15,750	1,850
18,700	2,664	17,200	2,228	15,700	1,836
18,650	2,650	17,150	2,215	15,650	1,824
18,600	2,635	17,100	2,202	15,600	1,813
18,550	2,619	17,050	2,187	15,550	1,799

Counts/min	Lost counts	Counts/min	Lost counts	Counts/min	Lost counts
15,500	1,788	13,350	1,306	11,200	904
15,450	1,776	13,300	1,295	11,150	896
15,400	1,763	13,250	1,285	11,100	888
15,350	1,751	13,200	1,275	11,050	879
15,300	1,740	13,150	1,264	11,000	871
15,250	1,727	13,100	1,255	10,950	864
15,200	1,715	13,050	1,245	10,900	855
15,150	1,704	13,000	1,234	10,850	847
15,100	1,691	12,950	1,225	10,800	838
15,050	1,680	12,900	1,215	10,750	830
15,000	1,667	12,850	1,204	10,700	823
14,950	1,656	12,800	1,195	10,650	815
14,900	1,645	12,750	1,186	10,600	806
14,850	1,634	12,700	1,175	10,550	799
14,800	1,621	12,650	1,166	10,500	790
14,750	1,610	12,600	1,157	10,450	783
14,700	1,599	12,550	1,146	10,400	776
14,650	1,586	12,500	1,137	10,350	768
14,600	1,575	12,450	1,128	10,300	760
14,550	1,565	12,400	1,118	10,250	753
14,500	1,552	12,350	1,109	10,200	745
14,450	1,542	12,300	1,100	10,150	737
14,400	1,531	12,250	1,090	10,100	730
14,350	1,519	12,200	1,081	10,050	723
14,300	1,508	12,150	1,072	10,000	715
14,250	1,498	12,100	1,062	9,950	708
14,200	1,485	12,050	1,054	9,900	701
14,150	1,475	12,000	1,043	9,850	693
14,100	1,465	11,950	1,035	9,800	686
14,050	1,453	11,900	1,026	9,750	679
14,000	1,442	11,850	1,018	9,700	672
13,950	1,432	11,800	1,008	9,650	664
13,900	1,420	11,750	1,000	9,600	658
13,850	1,410	11,700	991	9,550	650
13,800	1,400	11,650	981	9,500	643
13,750	1,388	11,600	973	9,450	636
13,700	1,378	11,550	965	9,400	629
13,650	1,368	11,500	955	9,350	622
13,600	1,357	11,450	947	9,300	616
13,550	1,347	11,400	939	9,250	608
13,500	1,335	11,350	930	9,200	602
13,450	1,325	11,300	922	9,150	595
13,400	1,316	11,250	913	9,100	588

Counts/ min	Lost counts	Counts/ min	Lost counts	Counts/ min	Lost counts
9,050	582	6,900	333	4,750	156
9,000	574	6,850	328	4,700	152
8,950	568	6,800	323	4,650	149
8,900	562	6,750	318	4,600	146
8,850	556	6,700	314	4,550	142
8,800	550	6,650	309	4,500	139
8,750	543	6,600	304	4,450	136
8,700	537	6,550	299	4,400	133
8,650	530	6,500	295	4,350	130
8,600	524	6,450	290	4,300	127
8,550	518	6,400	285	4,250	124
8,500	511	6,350	281	4,200	121
8,450	505	6,300	276	4,150	118
8,400	498	6,250	272	4,100	115
8,350	493	6,200	268	4,050	112
8,300	487	6,150	263	4,000	110
8,250	480	6,100	259	3,950	107
8,200	474	6,050	255	3,900	104
8,150	469	6,000	250	3,850	102
8,100	462	5,950	246	3,800	99
8,050	457	5,900	242	3,750	96
8,000	451	5,850	237	3,700	94
7,950	445	5,800	233	3,650	91
7,900	439	5,750	230	3,600	89
7,850	434	5,700	225	3,550	86
7,800	428	5,650	221	3,500	83
7,750	423	5,600	218	3,450	81
7,700	417	5,550	213	3,400	79
7,650	411	5,500	210	3,350	76
7,600	406	5,450	206	3,300	74
7,550	401	5,400	202	3,250	72
7,500	395	5,350	198	3,200	70
7,450	390	5,300	195	3,150	68
7,400	385	5,250	190	3,100	66
7,350	379	5,200	187	3,050	63
7,300	374	5,150	183	3,000	61
7,250	369	5,100	180	2,950	59
7,200	363	5,050	176	2,900	57
7,150	358	5,000	172	2,850	55
7,100	353	4,950	169	2,800	53
7,050	348	4,900	166	2,750	51
7,000	343	4,850	162	2,700	49
6,950	338	4,800	159	2,650	48

Counts/min	Lost counts	Counts/min	Lost counts	Counts/min	Lost counts
2,600	46	1,600	17	650	3
2,550	44	1,550	16	600	2
2,500	42	1,500	15	550	2
2,450	41	1,450	14	500	2
2,400	39	1,400	13	450	1
2,350	37	1,350	12	400	1
2,300	36	1,300	11	350	1
2,250	34	1,250	10	300	1
2,200	33	1,200	10	250	
2,150	31	1,150	9	200	
2,100	30	1,100	8	150	
2,050	28	1,050	7	100	
2,000	27	1,000	7	75	
1,950	25	950	6	50	
1,900	24	900	5	25	
1,850	23	850	5	20	
1,800	22	800	4	15	
1,750	21	750	4	10	
1,700	19	700	3	1	
1,650	18				

APPENDIX 4

List of Manufacturers

THE following list includes manufacturers whose products are most likely to be useful to schools or colleges undertaking elementary radioisotope work. It is intended only to be a useful guide, since it cannot be complete.

Airmec Ltd., High Wycombe, Bucks. (Nucleonic equipment.)

B.D.H. Ltd., Poole, Dorset. (Chemicals, including compounds of naturally occurring radioactive elements.)

Bendix Electronics Ltd., Basford, Nottingham. (Nucleonic equipment.)

Burndept Electronics Ltd., Erith, Kent. (Nucleonic equipment.)

Ealing Scientific Ltd., 23 Leman Street, London, E. 1. (Educational scientific equipment, including nucleonic apparatus.)

Ekco Electronics Ltd., Southend-on-Sea, Essex. (Nucleonic Equipment.)

E.M.I. Electronics Ltd., Instrument Division, Hayes, Middlesex. (Nucleonic equipment.)

E.R.D. Engineering, Ipswich Road, Slough, Bucks. (Lead shielding and other accessories.)

General Biological Supply House, 8200 South Hoyne Avenue, Chicago 20, Illinois, U.S.A. (Irradiated seeds for class experiments.)

Griffin & George Ltd., Ealing Road, Alperton, Wembley, Middlesex. (General educational scientific equipment, including that for school radioisotope work.)

P. Harris Ltd., Ludgate Hill, Birmingham, 3. (General educational scientific equipment, including that for school radioisotope work.)

Hopkin & Williams Ltd., Freshwater Road, Chadwell Heath, Essex. (Chemicals, including compounds of naturally occurring radioactive elements.)

Ilford Ltd., Ilford, Essex. (Photographic equipment, including X-ray film and nuclear emulsions.)

Isotope Developments Ltd., Bath Road, Beenham, Reading, Berkshire. (Nucleonic equipment.)

Jencons Ltd., Hemel Hempstead, Herts. (Radioactive labels and labelled apparatus.)

Jonpar Electronics, 44, Blenheim Gardens, Southampton. (Scalers etc.)

Kodak Ltd., Kingsway, London, W.C. 2. (Photographic equipment, including X-ray film and stripping film.)

Labgear Ltd., Willow Road, Cambridge. (Nucleonic equipment and an educational kit.)

M.E.L. Equipment Ltd., Manor Royal, Crawley, Sussex. (Nucleonic equipment.)

Morris Laboratory Instruments Ltd., 96–98 Putney High Street, London, S.W. 15. (General educational scientific equipment.)

M.O. Valve Co. Ltd., Brook Green, Hammersmith, London, W. 6. (Geiger tubes.)

Mullard Ltd., X-ray Division, Mitcham Junction, Surrey. (Geiger tubes.)

W. B. Nicholson Ltd., Thornliebank Industrial Estate, Glasgow, Scotland. (General educational scientific equipment.)

Nucleonic Accessories, Lee Green, Mirfield, Yorkshire. (Lead castles, planchets, filtration equipment suitable for radio-isotopes, absorbers, small educational type sources, etc.)

Panax Equipment Ltd., Holmethorpe Industrial Estate, Redhill, Surrey. (Nucleonic equipment and educational kits.)

J. A. Radley Ltd., 220 Elgar Road, Reading, Berks. (Radio-isotopes in tablet form.)

The Radiochemical Centre, Amersham, Bucks. (Radioactive sources and radiochemicals.)

Rainbow Radio Ltd., Mincing Lane, Blackburn. (Educational nucleonic equipment, etc.)

Rank Nucleonics and Controls Ltd., Welwyn Garden City, Herts. (Nucleonic equipment.)

Research Electronics Ltd., Cleckheaton, Yorks. (Nucleonic equipment.)

Scientific Teaching Apparatus Ltd., 27–37 Broadwick Street, London, W. 1. (General scientific educational equipment manufactured by the Leybold Company of Cologne.)

R. A. Stephen & Co. Ltd., 120–126 Lavender Avenue, Mitcham, Surrey. (Quartz fibre ionisation chambers for educational use and quartz fibre personnel dosimeters.)

Twentieth Century Electronics Ltd., King Henry's Drive, New Addington, Croydon, Surrey. (Geiger tubes, solid state detectors, etc.)

(Messrs. Nucleonic Consultants Ltd. of Argon House, Osmaston Road, Stourbridge, Worcestershire, provide a free advisory service to schools and colleges on the selection and installation of nucleonic equipment.)

References

1. DEARNALEY, G. and NORTHROP, D. C., *Semiconductor Counters for Nuclear Radiations*, Spon, London, 1964.
2. TAYLOR, J. M., *Semiconductor Particle Detectors*, Butterworth, London, 1963.
3. DANCE, J. B., Semiconductor detectors for nuclear radiation, *Wireless World* 71 (9), 442 (1965).
4. FRIEDLANDER, G. and KENNEDY, J. W., *Nuclear and Radiochemistry*, Wiley, New York, 1955.
5. BLEULER, E. and GOLDSMITH, G. J., *Experimental Nucleonics*, Holt, Rinehart & Winston, New York, 1952.
6. OVERMAN, R. T. and CLARK, H. M., *Radioisotope Techniques*, McGraw-Hill, New York, 1960.
7. *The Use of Ionising Radiations in Schools, Establishments of Further Education and Teacher Training Colleges*, Department of Education and Science, London, Administrative Memorandum 1/65, January 1965.
8. *Nucleonics Reference Data Manual*, McGraw-Hill, New York, 1960.
9. ALLEN, R. A., SMITH, D. B. and HISCOTT, J. E., *Radioisotope Data*, A.E.R.E. Report R2938, 1961.
10. *The Radiochemical Manual*, Part 1, Radiochemical Centre Amersham.
11. U.K.A.E.A. Technical Data Sheet No. 4.
12. DUNSTER, H. J., *An Anthology of Health Physics Data*, R. and D.B.(W) TN-58, 1957 (from H.M.S.O.).
13. *Code of Practice for the Protection of Persons exposed to Ionising Radiations in Research and Teaching*, Ministry of Labour, London, 1964.
14. *Notes for the Guidance of Technical Colleges concerned with the Use of Unsealed Radioactive Substances*, Ministry of Education, London, 1960.
15. *Recommendations of the International Committee on Radiological Protection*, Report of Committee II on Permissible Dose from Internal Radiation, Pergamon, Oxford, 1959.
16. *Radiation Protection Norms*, European Nuclear Energy Agency, Paris, 1963.
17. *The Use of Radioactive Substances for Work at Schools Level*, Notes I.R.N., Department of Education and Science, London, 1965.
18. J. A. RADLEY LTD., private communication, February 1966.
19. *A Decade Scaler*, Educational Electronic Experiments No. 9, Mullard Educational Service, London, 1964.
20. *Tube Technical Handbook*, Ericsson Telephones Ltd., Nottingham.
21. CHAPPELL, G. C. and JEYNES, G. F., *Transistor Coupling Circuits for the Z504S Stepping Tube*, Mullard Tech. Communications, 7, 70, 310 (1964).

22. JEYNES, G. F. and ZILKHA, S., *Trigger Tube Coupling Circuits for Counting Tubes*, Mullard Tech. Communications, 7, 60, 184 (1963).
23. JEYNES, G. F., *Decade Stepping Tubes and their Operation*, Mullard Tech. Communications, 4, 37, 194 (1959).
24. *Solid State Detectors*, Twentieth Century Electronics Ltd., Croydon, 1965.
25. *Collected Papers from Journal of Chemical Education related to Training and Experiments in Radioactivity*, Nuclear Chicago Corporation, Illinois, 1959.
26. *A Basic Course of Radioisotope Experiments*, Panax Equipment Ltd., Surrey, 1963.
27. COOK, G. B. and DUNCAN, J. F., *Modern Radiochemical Practice*, Oxford University Press, London, 1952.
28. SMIT, J. VAN R., JACOBS, J. J. and ROBB, W., Cation exchange properties of ammonium heteropolyacid salts, *J. Inorg. Nucl. Chem.* 12, 95 (1959).
29. HAXEL, O., Eine einfache Methode zur Messung des Gehaltes der Luft an radioacktiven Substanzen, *Z. Angew. Phys.* 15, 241 (1953).
30. PACKER, T. W., *The Determination of the Paralysis Time of an Electronically Quenched Probe Unit*, A.E.R.E. Report M1109, 1962.
31. Administrative Memorandum No. 547, Ministry of Education, London, 1957.
32. *Notes for the Guidance of Technical Colleges concerned with the Use of X-Rays and Sealed Radioactive Substances*, Ministry of Education, London, 1960.
33. Administrative Memorandum No. 577, Ministry of Education, London, 1958.
34. The Radioactive Substances Act, 1960 (from H.M.S.O.).
35. The Radioactive Substances Act, 1960. *An Explanatory Memorandum for Persons Keeping or Using Radioactive Materials*, H.M.S.O., 1963.
36. The Radioactive Substances (Schools etc.) Exemption Order, 1963, H.M.S.O.
37. *The Teaching of Modern Physics*, Nuffield Foundation and the Association for Science Education, 1964.

Literature on Radioisotope Experiments

Descriptions of various experiments with radioisotopes have been published in the references 4, 5, 6, 25, 26, 27 and 37 given above. In addition the following works may be consulted.

ARONOFF, S., *Techniques of Radiobiochemistry*, Iowa State College Press, 1956.
BROWN, B., *Experimental Nucleonics*, Iliffe, London, 1963.
CHASE, G. D., *Principles of Radioisotope Methodology*, Burgess Co., Minneapolis, 1960.
CHOPPIN, G. R., *Experimental Nuclear Chemistry*, Prentice-Hall, New York, 1961.

DANFORTH, J. P. and STAPP, R. P., *Radioisotopes in Industry. Training Program*, 2 vols., General Motors, 1959 (available from Office of Tech. Services, Washington, 25, D.C.).

FRIEDRICH, A., LANGEHEINE, H. and ULBRICHT, H., *Experiments in Atomic Physics*, J. Murray, London, 1966 (original version published in German by Aulis Verlag in 1960).

Experimental Notes, Griffin & George, Wembley, Middlesex (issued periodically).

LADD, M. F. C. and LEE, W. H., *Practical Radiochemistry*, Macmillan, London, 1964.

MINER, H. A., SHACKLETON, R. W. and WATSON, F. L., *Teaching with Radioisotopes*, U.S. Government Printing Office, Washington, 25, D.C., 1959.

OAK RIDGE INSTITUTE OF NUCLEAR STUDIES, Tennessee, various manuals of experiments.

PEACOCKE, T. H., The teaching of radioactivity in schools, *Bulletin of the Institute of Physics*, p. 115, April 1957.

PEACOCKE, T. H., Radioactive Isotopes, *Contemporary Physics* **4** (1) 62 (1962).

PEARSON, F. J. and OSBORNE, R. R., *Practical Nucleonics*, Spon, London, 1960.

Radioisotope Experiments for the Chemistry Curriculum, Nuclear Chicago and the United States Atomic Energy Commission, 1960 (2 vols.).

SCHENBERG, S., *Laboratory Experiments with Radioisotopes for High School Science Demonstrations*, U.S. Government Printing Office, 1958.

SEELMANN-EGGEBERT, W., *Radiochemischer Isotopenkurs*, Kernreaktor Bau- und Betriebs Gesellschaft, Karlsruhe, Germany.

SEELMANN-EGGEBERT, W., KELLER, C. and ZUNDEL, G., *Radiochemische Demonstrations-versuche*, Kernreaktor Bau- und Betriebs Gesellschaft, Karlsruhe, Germany.

Short Course in Basic and Applied Isotope Technology, W. H. Johnstone Labs., 1960 (available from Office of Tech. Services, Washington, 25, D.C.).

VOIGT, A. F., *A Laboratory Manual for Radiochemistry*, Iowa State College Press, 1960.

WAHL, A. C. and BONNER, N. A., *Radioactivity applied to Chemistry*, Wiley, New York, 1951.

WOODBURN, J. H., *Nuclear Science Teaching Aids and Activities*, Office of Education, Washington, D.C., 1959.

Literature on Nucleonic Instrumentation

DANCE, J. B., *Electronic Counting Circuits*, Iliffe, London, 1967.

KORFF, S. A. and KALLMANN, H., *Electron and Nuclear Counters*, Van Nostrand, London and New York, 1955.

Index